ANIMAL HYBRIDS G.

CANARY POP!T

THE INVENTIVE GAME OF WACKY WORDS AND DIPPY DOODLES

KING OF THE
BUMBLE

HOOTIE MOO

SHELL-SHOCKED BROCK

BASED ON AN ORIGINAL IDEA BY GRACE CLARKE
WORDS BY ALICE CLARKE

CANARY POP!T

The Inventive Game of Wacky Words and Dippy Doodles

1ˢᵗ Edition

ISBN (paperback) 978-1-7397993-0-4
ISBN (hardback) 978-1-7397993-1-1
ISBN (digital) 978-1-7397993-2-8

www.baggywrinkl.com

Illustrations: Alejandro Gil (and Elefairy by Ron Clarke)
Cover Design: Mairi Clarke

For Grace, Mairi and Zach

And for creatures everywhere

CANARY POP!T

THE INVENTIVE GAME OF WACKY WORDS AND DIPPY DOODLES

Playing Canary Pop!t is a great way to celebrate creature diversity (both real and imagined).
Discover fascinating facts, enjoy an amusing, creative game and express your own, original ideas.

Purchasing this book helps to support wildlife throughout the world.
10% from the sale of each book goes to help a number of animal-based charities.

CONTENTS

HOW TO PLAY

Object of the Game

Each player's aim is to create inventive pictures and original names for hybrid creatures, and in doing so, to gather as many points as possible. The winner is the person with the most points by the end of the game. (It's also a game that can be enjoyed simply for fun, with less focus on winning.)

To play the game, each player will need:

✓ A pile <u>of blank sheets of A5 paper</u> – one piece per round. Paper for all players should look the same.

✓ <u>A pen or a pencil</u> – a black marker each would be ideal. Again, the same colour for each person.

✓ <u>Something to lean on</u> – a hardback book or similar, to allow players to draw in secret.

✓ The group will also need <u>a scoresheet</u>.

(There are scoresheet examples in the back of the book for different lengths of games. You're welcome to copy these, print out spares from our website – baggywrinkl.com – or you could easily just use a blank piece of paper to create your own.)

Rules

<u>3 or more people of almost any age can play</u> – the more players, the better (within reason!).
<u>All words should be written in capital letters</u> in order to try to disguise who has written what.
It's also a good idea to <u>try not to give away your drawing style</u>, although this isn't always possible.

1. Choose someone to be the **CANARY**. The Canary's job is to make decisions about **CHOOSERS**, show everyone the relevant pictures, read out facts, gather in and lay out pieces of paper, organise the voting and keep the score.

2. The **CANARY** picks two people who are sitting next to each other to begin the first round. These people are the first two **CHOOSERS**. (Once the first round has been played, the next two **CHOOSERS** will be those to the left of the first two, and so on.) The **CANARY** is at liberty to decide whether he/she would also like to be one of the two **CHOOSERS** during the game or not.

3. The two **CHOOSERS** each decide on a different number from 1 to 20. They then find their separate numbers in the **PICK AND MIX** part of the book. Each **CHOOSER** then selects one of the seven creatures listed on their particular page and declares which one they've chosen.

4. The **CANARY** then finds each creature in the **DID YOU KNOW?** section, shows everyone the two images, and reads out some or all of the information about the two chosen creatures. (Discovering more about each creature helps players with both their hybrid name ideas and picture designs.)

5. However, it's just as possible to play the game with only the pictures (i.e. without reading out the information), which might be more suitable for younger groups. Doing it this way also makes the game go a little quicker. Each group will differ as to what works best, and it's up to the **CANARY** to decide how much or how little from the **DID YOU KNOW?** pages they read out.)

6. Everyone (including the **CANARY**) then takes their pen/pencil, paper, and something to lean on and secretly begins to draw a unique hybrid – a combination of the two chosen creatures, then gives it a name. Inventive illustrations and original name ideas are endless – especially with 140 different creatures to combine and in countless possible ways! You'll find tips about how to come up with brilliant ideas from the **DRAWING DESIGNS** and **NAME GAME** sections, following on from this.

7. Once all the names and pictures have been secretly written/drawn, everyone hands their piece of paper face-down to the **CANARY**, who waits until he/she has them all. The **CANARY** then mixes up the order of the pieces of paper and turns them face-up, one at a time, laying them out for everyone to see.

8. The **CANARY** then writes a different number on the picture side of each piece of paper (e.g. 1 – 6 if there are six players), then attempts to say each creature's name out loud, preferably without stumbling over the inventive names – not always an easy task! The aim at this point is for everyone, including the **CANARY**, to try not to give away which picture/name they have created.

9. Players should now consider which creature (identified by its number) they like best – bearing in mind, of course, that no-one is allowed to vote for their own creation. Criteria for voting is decided upon individually. One person might like a certain name because it's especially clever, another person might like a particular drawing as it captures a funny way that the creatures were combined, and so on...

10. Time to vote. Everyone closes their fists, then after the count of three by the **CANARY**, all players reveal their favourite hybrid by holding up the appropriate number of fingers – based on the different numbers that the **CANARY** has just written on the different pieces of paper. For games with 10 – 20 players, feet can also be used, each foot representing 'five'.

11. Points are awarded – one point for every vote each person gets. One point is taken off for any **CANARY CLONES** – when two or more people come up with identical names.

12. If anyone gets voted for by **everyone else** in the group, that person becomes **THE CAT THAT GOT THE CANARY** for that round and gets a further 2 points!

A note about collective nouns:

Collective nouns are quite difficult to pin down. There are some that are very well-known and commonly used, and others that are much more obscure. It can also be unclear whether some collective nouns are actually in use or not, or are just great ideas that someone once had. Plus, for some creatures, there are only one or two collective nouns and for others there are lots – which can depend on where the creature is (in the air, on land, in water etc.), what they're doing (eating, sleeping, standing etc.), as well as their age, gender, size of group – and even whether they have or haven't had young. A variety of these collective nouns have been included in the **DID YOU KNOW?** section, depending on each specific creature. In addition, a little poetic licence has been used to add in a few more possibilities that came to mind – but which aren't collective nouns at all. These have all just been combined for the sake of simplicity.

Some extra food for thought (for once you've played the game a few times):

Canary Pop!t is a very flexible game, and you may find you come up with other ideas for different types of rounds and/or other ways to score. The collective noun possibilities in the **DID YOU KNOW?** section, for example, could be used to try to invent collective nouns for your hybrid creatures. Or you may want to try a round of drawing the male, female and juvenile of a combined creature. And other well-known canary sayings ('to sing like a canary' and 'canary in a coal mine', for example) might inspire other ideas too. Or...

<u>Go to baggywrinkl.com to watch a video on how to play the game.</u>

DRAWING DESIGNS

Top Tips for Creating Inventive Hybrid Pictures

Sketching an imaginative Canary Pop!t creature is all about considering the unique physical aspects of both creatures and then combining them in an interesting way. Two unique aspects of a giraffe, for example, are its long neck and the type of pattern on its body. It's also the tallest mammal on Earth, has a very long tongue, and two ossicones (the horn-like structures) on top of its head. Considering these facts and any facts you know/discover about the other creature you are blending it with, will help you to design your own original creature.

Or, say the two animals you had to combine were a moose and a ladybird/ladybug. A moose's uniqueness lies partly in its amazingly large, velvety antlers and possibly also the iconic shape of its face. The ladybird is especially well-known for its spots. These features would be the most obvious to combine in your hybrid. Moose also have long legs, hooves, a large body, and a tail, while ladybirds/ladybugs have thin legs, wings and antennae. The two examples below are just two fairly simple ways that these creatures could be combined. When you look through the rest of the book, you'll find many more ideas to spark lots of other inventive ways to explore creature hybrid creativity.

DRAWING ABILITY

Some words of reassurance...

There are lots of pictures of hybrids throughout the Canary Pop!t book, and some people playing the game might wonder how they'll ever manage to draw as well as these. Please don't worry at all. Drawing ability is only a small part of the game. People often vote for a hybrid because it looks sweet, makes them smile, or just because it captures something in a certain way. Below is the original picture of Elefairy, which, although fairly simple, still manages to capture an adorable creature with a little wand in its trunk, rising into the air.

Elefairy

NAME GAME

Top Tips for Inventing Interesting Hybrid Names

What you decide to call your hybrid creatures will depend on a variety of factors. If the two creatures you want to combine are a slug and a hippopotamus, for example, one idea might be to call your hybrid a **slugopotamus**. A butterfly plus a kangaroo could be a **butteroo**. And a frog combined with a goat could simply be a **froat**. However, to avoid coming up with the same name as anyone else (see **CANARY CLONES** - page 2), and to inspire others to vote for your creation, it may wiser to be slightly more inventive.

The **DID YOU KNOW?** pages provide lots of words and information for name-generating inspiration. Going back to the example of a slug and a hippopotamus, a slug is a gastropod (Latin for stomach-foot), so, a **gastropodamus** might be a more interesting option to go for. Slugs are also slimy and sticky and make clear trails when they move. Based on these facts, other ideas might be a **hippo-sticki-mus**, a **hippytrailypod**, a **stickypod** or even a **hippo-poddy-gastro-slimy-mus**! The more inventive you are, the more fun and potential points there are to be had.

It's also worth considering **suitable descriptive words**, such as: lesser, greater, aquatic, domestic, feathered, giant, horned, lop-eared, migratory, spineless, tufted, man-eating, poisonous, web-footed, winged, territorial etc... The **greater spiral-horned grizzlycorn** (grizzly bear + unicorn), the **velvet-antlered dot bug** (moose + ladybird/ladybug) and the **wandering hee-haw** (albatross + donkey) are a few examples of these. You'll come across all sorts of these types of animal-based adjectives when you read about the various species in the **DID YOU KNOW?** section.

As Canary Pop!t is all about being inventive, there's also nothing to stop you including some **personification**. Adding in a name or a title – or both – can bring in extra elements of fun too. Some useful titles to consider might be: Mr, Mrs, Ms, Master, Sir, Madam, Doctor, Right Honourable, President, Mayor, Mayoress, Provost, Prince, Princess, Grand Duke, Duchess, Marquis, Empress, Lord, Lady, Captain, etc. A pig + parrot hybrid could be **Sir Beaky Snorty-squawk**; a butterfly + kangaroo could be **Miss Sheila Flutter-Jumper**, and a lion + bee could be **Mr Roary McBuzz**.

And a last word on creativity. **Jokes, puns, alliteration, irony, onomatopoeia, assonance, oxymorons,** etc. are all good ways to bring in a clever twist or two to your name idea. Here are a few of these types of ideas: **King of the Bumble** (lion +bee), **T'wit, T'moo** (owl + cow), **'Sss Pink Innit (Cockney accent required)** (snake + flamingo).

One of the best aspects of Canary Pop!t is that you can be as innovative as you like.

MISS SHEILA FLUTTER-JUMPER

HOPPITY FLITTY

SKIPPY FLUTTERBY

COMMON BUTTEROO

SPIRAL-HORNED GRIZZLE-MONSTER

SNUB-NOSED GRIZZLY-CORN

GIANT UNI-URSUS

ENCHANTED SPARKLE-BEAR

KING OF THE BUMBLE

MR ROARY McBUZZ

LORD LEO STINGER

KING-AND-QUEEN BEAST

PICK AND MIX

Each CHOOSER decides on a number from 1 to 20 then selects one of the seven creatures from their chosen page. The small numbers beside each creature make it quicker to find them in the DID YOU KNOW? section.

1

KINGFISHER$_{64}$

SQUIRREL$_{118}$

DODO$_{31}$

SLUG$_{114}$

SEAHORSE$_{107}$

ARMADILLO$_{4}$

GIANT$_{47}$

2

HUMMINGBIRD$_{61}$

HORSE$_{60}$

PORCUPINE$_{97}$

STARFISH$_{119}$

GOLDFISH$_{52}$

TOAD$_{127}$

PTERODACTYL$_{100}$

3

EAGLE$_{39}$

SHEEP$_{111}$

TIGER$_{126}$

CATERPILLAR$_{17}$

EEL$_{40}$

TURTLE$_{129}$

BRONTOSAURUS$_{12}$

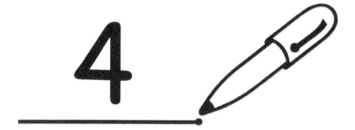

4

5

DUCK$_{38}$

CHIMPANZEE$_{23}$

SEAL$_{109}$

MOTH$_{80}$

CLOWN FISH$_{24}$

LIZARD$_{69}$

CENTAUR$_{18}$

6

OSTRICH$_{85}$

LEOPARD$_{67}$

HIPPOPOTAMUS$_{58}$

SNAIL$_{115}$

SQUID$_{117}$

PLATYPUS$_{95}$

TYRANNOSAURUS REX$_{130}$

7

PENGUIN$_{92}$

GRIZZLY BEAR$_{56}$

GOAT$_{51}$

COCKROACH$_{25}$

SHARK$_{110}$

FROG$_{45}$

UNICORN$_{131}$

8

SWAN$_{121}$

GORILLA$_{54}$

OTTER$_{86}$

CRICKET$_{29}$

JELLYFISH$_{62}$

GECKO$_{46}$

GRIFFIN$_{55}$

9

DOVE$_{35}$

CAMEL$_{14}$

BADGER$_5$

TARANTULA$_{124}$

PRAWN$_{98}$

TORTOISE$_{128}$

GNOME$_{50}$

10

VULTURE$_{133}$

GIRAFFE$_{49}$

CAT$_{16}$

MOSQUITO$_{79}$

DOLPHIN$_{33}$

TADPOLE$_{123}$

MINOTAUR$_{76}$

11

CHICKEN$_{22}$

MOUSE$_{81}$

ELEPHANT$_{41}$

ANT$_2$

LOBSTER$_{71}$

CROCODILE$_{30}$

FAIRY$_{42}$

12

WOODPECKER138

ORANGUTAN84

SKUNK113

WORM139

SWORDFISH122

BEARDED DRAGON7

PHOENIX93

13

CANARY$_{15}$

GIANT PANDA$_{48}$

SHETLAND PONY$_{112}$

BEETLE$_{10}$

WALRUS$_{134}$

MEERKAT$_{74}$

MERMAID$_{75}$

14

GOOSE$_{53}$

DOG$_{32}$

ZEBRA$_{140}$

CENTIPEDE$_{19}$

CRAB$_{28}$

SALAMANDER$_{105}$

LOCH NESS MONSTER$_{72}$

15

PEACOCK$_{89}$

HEDGEHOG$_{57}$

FOX$_{44}$

SCORPION$_{106}$

WHALE$_{137}$

ANTEATER$_{3}$

HOBBIT$_{59}$

16

BIRD-OF-PARADISE$_{11}$

RHINOCEROS$_{104}$

BAT$_{6}$

WASP$_{135}$

MANTA RAY$_{73}$

RABBIT$_{102}$

DRAGON$_{36}$

17

18

ALBATROSS$_1$

MOLE$_{77}$

DONKEY$_{34}$

BUTTERFLY$_{13}$

SEA URCHIN$_{108}$

KANGAROO$_{63}$

STEGOSAURUS$_{120}$

19

PARROT$_{88}$

PIG$_{94}$

LION$_{68}$

BEE$_9$

NARWHAL$_{82}$

RAT$_{103}$

PEGASUS$_{90}$

20

DID YOU KNOW?

The following pages reveal images and fascinating facts about each creature.
Use what you discover here to help you create unique and inventive hybrids.

1. ALBATROSS

Description: Albatrosses are seabirds with a huge wingspan of up to 12 feet and are the world's largest flying birds. The different species are various combinations of black, white, brown and grey.

Albatross words: Albatross species include the WANDERING, SNOWY and WHITE-WINGED ALBATROSS – once commonly known as GOONIE/GOONY birds.

Did you know? 1: Albatrosses have mastered the art of soaring flight and can glide for miles without having to flap their wings.

Did you know? 2: There are many stories surrounding albatrosses, often connected to sailors. Seeing an albatross flying overhead could mean good luck (if the sailors believed that a lost sailor's soul was protecting them or bringing them the winds they needed). Or, it could mean bad luck (the sign of someone's imminent death). Killing or eating an albatross was also thought to bring bad luck.

Did you know? 3: Albatrosses spend up to 80% of their time flying over the ocean.

Collective noun possibilities: COLONY, ROOKERY, WEIGHT, DRIFT, FLOAT, COAST

2. ANT

Description: Ants are insects with elbowed antennae, a long thin thorax (between the neck and the abdomen), and a large abdomen. Their head includes powerful mandibles (jaws).

Ant words: Ant species include the PHARAOH, BANDED SUGAR, FIRE, ELECTRIC, JACK JUMPER, SMALL HONEY and BULLET ANT (said to give the most painful sting in the world). Ants are from the FORMICIDAE family.

Did you know? 1: Ants live in large groups called colonies and work together for the benefit of the group as a whole. The largest super-colony ever found was in Argentina where 33 huge ant populations had merged together, creating one giant super-colony that was 3,700 miles wide!

Did you know? 2: Ants can be found on every continent - except ANTarctica!

Did you know? 3: Of all the world's insects, ants have the capacity to live the longest. Some insects live for just a few days or even hours, but there's one particular queen ant that can live for up to 30 years.

Collective noun possibilities: COLONY, NEST, SWARM, FORMICARY

3. ANTEATER

Description: Anteaters are small to medium-sized mammals with an elongated snout and a very long thin, sticky tongue that is covered in tiny hooks. They also have a tube-shaped mouth with no teeth and large, curved fore-claws.

Anteater words: The four types of anteater are the GIANT and SILKY ANTEATERS as well as the NORTHERN and SOUTHERN TAMANDUA ANTEATERS (also known as LESSER ANTEATERS). Anteaters belong to the suborder VERMILINGUA, meaning 'WORM TONGUE'. The giant anteater, due to its size and markings, is sometimes called the ANT BEAR.

Did you know? 1: Anteaters have poor sight but an excellent sense of smell.

Did you know? 2: They usually move very slowly. They can, however (if scared or startled, for example), reach speeds of up to 30mph.

Did you know? 3: As their name suggests, anteaters eat ants. They also eat a lot of termites – and sometimes fruit, birds' eggs, worms and other insects.

Collective noun possibilities: CANDLE – although anteaters are mostly solitary

4. ARMADILLO

Description: Armadillos are mammals with a leathery shell and long, sharp claws.

Armadillo words: Armadillo species include the PINK FAIRY ARMADILLO (the smallest one), various HAIRY ARMADILLOS, the SIX-BANDED ARMADILLO and the GIANT ARMADILLO (the largest). Armadillo means 'LITTLE ARMOURED ONE' in Spanish. The Aztecs called them TURTLE-RABBITS.

Did you know? 1: Armadillos have some interesting methods of defence. Brazilian and Southern three-banded armadillos can roll up into a ball, and the screaming hairy armadillo defends itself with very loud screeching sounds.

Did you know? 2: They are nocturnal creatures and spend up to 16 hours a day asleep.

Did you know? 3: Armadillos are good swimmers and diggers.

Collective noun possibilities: ROLL, HOOVER, ARRANGEMENT, HERD, PACK, BALL PIT

5. BADGER

Description: A badger is a medium-sized mammal with a short, wide body, an elongated head and small ears. A badger's head usually has a distinctive striped pattern and its tail varies in length depending on the species.

Badger words: Scientists tend to agree that the EURASIAN BADGER, the ASIAN HOG BADGER and the NORTH AMERICAN BADGER are TRUE BADGERS – less so the HONEY BADGER. The word badger comes from the French verb BECHER, to dig. BROCK is Old English for badger. The male is a BOAR, the female a SOW, and the young are CUBS.

Did you know? 1: Badgers often comfort their young during thunderstorms.

Did you know? 2: They are great at digging, and create elaborate tunnels called setts or dens.

Did you know? 3: Badgers vary as to how sociable they are. Eurasian badgers are the most sociable, often sharing resources as well as the tunnels they've created.

Collective noun possibilities: CETE, COLONY

6. BAT

Description: Bats are smallish mammals with fur-covered bodies and wings. Their wings are elongated finger bones that have a thin membrane of skin between them.

Bat words: Bat species include the COMMON PIPISTRELLE, BROWN LONG-EARED, LESSER HORSESHOE, WHISKERED, GREATER MOUSE-EARED, SILVER-HAIRED and COMMON VAMPIRE BAT. The largest bats – MEGA BATS – are also known as FRUIT BATS or FLYING FOXES. An Old English word for a bat is 'FLITTERMOUSE'.

Did you know? 1: Bats are the only mammals that can truly fly and are more agile than most birds.

Did you know? 2: Most bats are either insectivores or frugivores (fruit-eaters). Vampire bats feed on blood.

Did you know? 3: All bats (except fruit bats) use echolocation (sending out high frequency sound waves then listening to the echoes) to navigate and to find food.

Collective noun possibilities: COLONY, HANGER, CLOUD, CAULDRON, CAMP

7. BEARDED DRAGON

Description: Bearded dragons are reptiles with a 'beard' – an area made up of spikes, which sometimes puffs up and changes colour. Bearded dragons come in a variety of different colours, sizes and patterns.

Bearded dragon words: Bearded dragons that have been bred selectively to have a specific colour, pattern or general appearance are called MORPHS. These include the CLASSIC, LEATHERBACK, TRANSLUCENT, SILKBACK and PARADOX MORPH. The scientific name for a bearded dragon is POGONA. They are also affectionately known as BEARDIES.

Did you know? 1: Beardies are generally sweet-natured and curious.

Did you know? 2: They have a third eye located at the top of their head. It doesn't look or work like their other two eyes, but it does provide them with important information and is used primarily to detect light.

Did you know? 3: Cold-blooded, bearded dragons like to bask in the sun, often on trees or fence posts as they are also semi-arboreal.

Collective noun possibilities: BASK, LOUNGE, WHISKER, MUTTON-CHOP

8. BEAVER

Description: A beaver is a fairly big, semiaquatic rodent with a large head and a stocky body. Beavers also have long incisors (front teeth) and a flat, scaly tail.

Beaver words: There are only two beaver species – the NORTH AMERICAN BEAVER and the EURASIAN BEAVER.

Fun fact 1: Beavers are mainly nocturnal.

Fun fact 2: They are often used to represent hard work – for example, 'to beaver away', to be 'as busy as a beaver' and to be 'an eager beaver'.

Fun fact 3: Beavers build lodges to live in. These are dome-shaped structures made from sticks and mud.

Collective noun possibilities: COLONY, FAMILY, TEAMWORK, COOPERATION, HARMONY, ENDEAVOUR, ASSIGNMENT, MUSCLE, STRIVE, EXERTION, TOIL, HUSTLE, DILIGENCE

9. BEE

Description: Bees are insects with a pair of large, compound eyes as well as three small, simple eyes, which detect light. They have mandibles for chewing and a long proboscis for sucking up nectar. Only female bees have stingers.

Bee words: Types of bees include HONEY, BUMBLE, LEAF-CUTTER, WOOL-CARDER, FLOWER, NOMAD and LONG-HORNED BEES. Within a colony of honey bees, each bee does a specific job, including the QUEEN BEE, who lays eggs in cells within the comb. There are also WORKER BEES, DRONES, GUARDS, HONEY-MAKERS, ARCHITECTS and ATTENDANTS TO THE QUEEN.

Fun fact 1: Only honeybees specifically produce honey, using it as their main source of energy. Bees also feed on nectar (mainly for energy) and pollen (mainly for protein and other essential nutrients).

Fun fact 2: Bees are very important pollinators. They pollinate plants that we need to survive as well as certain trees and flowers that provide essential habitats for wildlife.

Fun fact 3: Despite having a brain the size of a sesame seed, bees can still be trained to detect diseases, sniff out bombs and even remember different human faces.

Collective noun possibilities: COLONY, NEST, STAND, RABBLE, SWARM, BIKE, CHARM, CLUSTER, DRIFT, ERST, GAME, GRIST, CAST, FRY, HIVE, HUM, COMB, BLOSSOM

10. BEETLE

Description: Beetles are insects with hardened, shield-like forewings. Like butterflies, beetles undergo complete metamorphosis: egg to larva to pupa to adult.

Beetle words: There are lots of different beetle families, including GROUND, LEAF, LONGHORN, SCARAB and ROVE BEETLES – as well as WEEVILS.

Did you know? 1: Some beetles are aposematic (brightly coloured to warn that they're toxic). Others are similar colours to their environment, which is great for camouflage.

Did you know? 2: Most beetles can fly, but a lot of their time is spent on the ground amongst low vegetation.

Did you know? 3: Beetles tend to communicate using pheromones, sounds and vibrations.

Collective noun possibilities: COLONY, SWARM, SHIELD

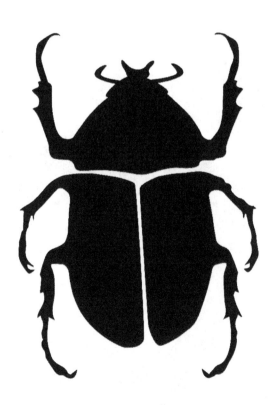

11. BIRD OF PARADISE

Description: Birds-of-paradise are known for their bright colours and elaborate plumage – long feathers, which come from their head, wings and/or tail, depending on the particular species.

Bird-of-paradise words: Bird-of-paradise species include the MAGNIFICENT, TWELVE-WIRED and EMPEROR BIRD-OF-PARADISE.

Did you know? 1: They are some of the world's most breath-taking and theatrical birds.

Did you know? 2: Birds-of-paradise mainly live on the island of Papua New Guinea, and in Indonesia and North-East Australia.

Did you know? 3: Females choose a male according to his plumage, the construction of his nest, his song and the quality of his elaborate courting display.

Collective noun possibilities: ELEGANCE, FASCINATION, MARVEL, FEAT, TRIUMPH, TOUR DE FORCE – although most birds-of-paradise are solitary tree-dwellers.

12. BRONTOSAURUS

Description: A brontosaurus was a gigantic, quadrupedal (four-footed), herbivorous dinosaur. It had a long neck, a small head, a heavy body and a long tail.

Brontosaurus words: Brontosaurus means THUNDER LIZARD and is also known as an APATOSAURUS.

Did you know? 1: The adult dinosaurs probably weighed up to 15 tonnes.

Did you know? 2: Computer modelling of the tail of a brontosaurus suggests that they may have been able to crack their tails in a whip-like motion, creating a noise as loud as a cannon (around 200 decibels).

Did you know? 3: The brontosaurus would have been a very slow-moving dinosaur.

Collective noun possibilities: THUNDER, THUNDER-CRACK

13. BUTTERFLY

Description: A butterfly is a flying insect with a small, thin body and four large, often brightly coloured wings, each made up of tiny scales. Butterflies usually have club-shaped antennae. They also have a flexible feeding tube (their proboscis).

Butterfly words: Butterfly species include the MONARCH, ZEBRA LONG-WING, RED ADMIRAL, QUEEN ALEXANDRA'S BIRDWING, MIAMI BLUE and PAINTED LADY. There's a story that the word for butterfly used to be FLUTTERBY, but this, it seems, is not actually true.

Did you know? 1: Butterflies go through a four-stage cycle, during which they undergo complete metamorphosis: egg – caterpillar – pupa – butterfly. Because of this, butterflies have represented the human soul throughout many cultures. For Christians, the steps of metamorphosis represent the spiritual transformation from the lowly caterpillar (earthly soul) to the stunning butterfly (the fulfilment of spiritual potential through a relationship with God).

Did you know? 2: They need heat to be able to move.

Did you know? 3: Butterflies taste with their feet.

Collective noun possibilities: SWARM, KALEIDOSCOPE, FLUTTER, RABBLE, WING, FLIGHT, FLOCK, RAINBOW, DANCE, PIROUETTE, SHIMMY, WHIRL

14. CAMEL

Description: A camel is a ruminant mammal with long legs, either one or two humps on its back, a large mouth, and big, thick lips. The top lip is split in two. Camels also have three sets of eyelids and two rows of eyelashes to keep sand out of their eyes.

Camel words: There are three species of camels left in the world today: the one-humped DROMEDARY (94% of the world camel population), the two-humped BACTRIAN camel (most of the remaining 6%) and the WILD BACTRIAN camel (now critically endangered).

Did you know? 1: Camels are famous for being able to withstand very hot desert conditions. Their humps are made of fatty tissue, which, when lacking a source of food, they can live off for weeks at a time.

Did you know? 2: They are able to completely shut their nostrils during a sandstorm.

Did you know? 3: Camels sometimes spit at whatever they feel threatened by.

Collective noun possibilities: CARAVAN, HERD, FLOCK, TRAIN, SCORN, DUNE, BULGE, BUMP, MOUND, HUMMOCK, HUNCH, HILLSIDE, LANDSCAPE

15. CANARY

Description: A canary, the natural symbol of the Canary Islands, is a small bird (typically about 4 inches long) from the finch family. The iconic Atlantic canary, aka the wild canary, is greenish-yellow.

Canary words: Canary species include the AMERICAN SINGER, BELGIAN FANCY, FRILLED and HARLEQUIN PORTUGUESE CANARY. TWEETY PIE, a canary in the Warner Brothers' cartoons, is probably the most famous canary of all. There are a number of well-known canary sayings: CANARY IN A COAL MINE means an early warning of danger; THE CAT THAT GOT THE CANARY means to appear smugly pleased, and TO SING LIKE A CANARY means to inform against someone. CANARY CLONES is a term used specifically in Canary Pop!t, when two or more people create exactly the same name for their hybrid and in doing so, each automatically loses a point.

Fun fact 1: Although yellow is the most common colour of the domestic canary, they can also be orange, red, white and dozens of other colours too.

Fun fact 2: Canaries are well-known for their melodious songs. Female song canaries mainly chirp, while males tend to develop elaborate tunes.

Fun fact 3: Canaries are naturally friendly birds.

Collective noun possibilities: ARIA, OPERA, WARBLE, CHOIR, CHANT, DESCANT, HARMONY

16. CAT

Description: Cats are smallish mammals with a strong, lithe body, sharp teeth, pointy ears, retractable claws, and whiskers.

Cat words: Cat breeds include the AMERICAN BOBTAIL, BENGAL, BURMESE, CALICO, DOMESTIC SHORTHAIR, JAVANESE, MAINE COON, MANX, MUNCHKIN, PERSIAN, PIXIEBOB, RAGAMUFFIN, RAGDOLL, SIAMESE, SPHYNX (HAIRLESS CAT), TORTOISESHELL, TOYGER and TABBY. A male cat is a TOM or TOMCAT. An unspayed female cat is a QUEEN. Baby cats are KITTENS. A (now obsolete) Early Modern English word for a baby cat is a CATLING. A cat is sometimes also called a MOUSER. Cats are known to MEOW and PURR.

Did you know? 1: Some cats can jump up to five times their own height and often perch in high places.

Did you know? 2: In Ancient Egypt, Egyptians believed cats were sacred creatures and that keeping one would bring good luck. They were highly honoured, and some people even dressed their cats in jewels!

Did you know? 3: When cats feel threatened, they sometimes raise their fur to appear larger.

Collective noun possibilities: GLARING, POUNCE, CLOWDER, CLUSTER (cats); LITTER, KINDLE, INTRIGUE, ENTANGLEMENT (kittens); DESTRUCTION (wild cats)

17. CATERPILLAR

Description: A caterpillar is the larval stage of moths and butterflies. Caterpillars have soft bodies and continue to shed their outer layer as they grow. They can be stripy, horned and/or hairy. Some are dangerous.

Caterpillar words: Caterpillar species include the HICKORY HORNED DEVIL, MONARCH CATERPILLAR, BLACK SWALLOWTAIL CATERPILLAR, WOOLLY BEAR and the ELEPHANT HAWK MOTH CATERPILLAR. The Scottish term 'HAIRY OOBIT', simply means 'hairy caterpillar' and is used to refer to any of the hairier caterpillar species. The VERY HUNGRY CATERPILLAR is a well-known character from the children's book of the same name by Eric Carle.

Did you know? 1: Caterpillars are typically voracious eaters – mostly vegetarian – and as a result can cause significant crop damage for farmers and gardeners.

Did you know? 2: Some caterpillar species are highly valued as producers of silk.

Did you know? 3: The number of legs a caterpillar has varies according to the species. Most caterpillars of larger butterflies and moths have 3 pairs of true legs and 5 pairs of pro legs – 16 legs in total.

Collective noun possibilities: ARMY, CHOMP, MUNCH, AMBITION

18. CENTAUR

Description: A centaur is a creature that originated in Greek mythology and has the upper body and head of a human and the lower body and legs of a horse.

Centaur words: CHIRON was said to be the first centaur and is also possibly the best known. He was different to most of the others as he was a divine being born from a cloud and was an incredibly wise teacher and great healer. NESSUS was a famous centaur who was not so refined.

Did you know? 1: Many centaurs were followers of Dionysus, the God of Wine, and most tended towards chaotic and rowdy behaviour.

Did you know? 2: Centaur superpowers are extraordinary strength and stamina.

Did you know? 3: They are able to use their front hooves as weapons.

Collective noun possibilities: EMINENCE, DISORDER, ANARCHY, PANDEMONIUM

19. CENTIPEDE

Description: A centipede is a predatory myriapod ('many feet'). They have a long, thin body made from segments, with one pair of legs on each segment, either a rounded or a flat head, and a pair of antennae.

Centipede words: Centipede species include the GIANT DESERT, TIGER, FEATHER TAIL, HOFFMAN'S DWARF and the TANZANIAN BLUE RING CENTIPEDE. The AMAZONIAN GIANT CENTIPEDE (aka the PERUVIAN GIANT YELLOW-LEG CENTIPEDE) can grow to over twelve inches long and is known to eat mice, birds, frogs and lizards. Centipedes also have a variety of nicknames, including WIGGLES, SIR LEGS-A-LOT and MISTER MANDIBLES.

Did you know? 1: Many centipedes are venomous, although their bites are not generally fatal to humans.

Did you know? 2: Very occasionally, centipedes can become lodged inside a person's ear.

Did you know? 3: Although centipede means 'hundred feet', the number of feet that centipedes actually have varies greatly – and none have exactly 100 feet, as they always have an odd number of legs!

Collective noun possibilities: SWARM, MARCH, PROMENADE, SCUTTLE, STEP, HIKE

20. CHAMELEON

Description: A chameleon is a specialised breed of old world lizard with eyes that work independently and a prehensile tail. They also have zygodactyl feet (two toes facing forwards and two backwards) and crests or horns on their brow and snout.

Chameleon words: Some chameleon species are the CARPET, ANGEL'S, JEWELLED and BLACK-HEADED DWARF CHAMELEON. Baby chameleons are called HATCHLINGS. Metaphorically, the word 'chameleon' is interchangeable with OPPORTUNIST, PRETENDER or someone who is FICKLE. Someone who changes their behaviour or beliefs to please others or to succeed is thought of as a POLITICAL CHAMELEON.

Did you know? 1: Chameleons feed by ballistically projecting their long, extendible tongue, mainly to catch insects.

Did you know? 2: Some species of chameleons have biogenic fluorescence (their bones glow through their skin when under ultraviolet light).

Did you know? 3: Chameleons have an ability to change the colour of their skin according to their temperature and mood. Some are able to change colour faster than others and some have a wider range of colour options.

Collective noun possibilities: CAMOUFLAGE, SWITCH, SHIFT, TRANSFORMATION

21. CHEETAH

Description: A cheetah is a large, lightly-built member of the cat family, with a small head, long legs, and a long tail. It has a tawny coat with distinctive black spots and black streaks on its face.

Cheetah words: 'Cheetah' comes from the Hindi word 'CHITA', meaning 'SPOTTED ONE'. In the past, cheetahs were sometimes called HUNTING LEOPARDS as they could be tamed and trained in coursing (the sport of hunting game animals by sight rather than scent). A KING CHEETAH is a rare breed of cheetah which, as well as spots, has three thick black stripes down its back.

Did you know? 1: The cheetah is famous for being the fastest land animal and can run at approx. 70 mph.

Did you know? 2: Cheetahs don't make scary, roaring sounds like some big cats – they meow and purr and make other gentle noises.

Did you know? 3: Some pharaohs in Ancient Egypt kept cheetahs as hunting companions.

Collective noun possibilities: COALITION, PURSUIT, STALKING

22. CHICKEN

Description: Chickens are medium-sized birds that can't fly very well – more of a hop and a flap. Both males and females have fleshy appendages: a comb (on top of their heads) and two wattles (below the chin), those on males usually being larger. Males are generally bigger with longer, more feathery tails.

Chicken words: Both males and females are known as CHICKENS. Gender, age and maturity are all factors in the more specific name used. A ROOSTER is an adult male; a COCKEREL is a young adult male; a HEN is a female that's over a year old, and a PULLET is a female that's under a year. Babies are CHICKS.

Did you know? 1: Chickens can learn to recognise their own name.

Did you know? 2: Combs and wattles help to regulate temperature.

Did you know? 3: Chickens enjoy a variety of activities including running, skipping, flapping their wings, having dust baths and sunbathing.

Collective noun possibilities: FLOCK, BROOD, PEEP, CLUTCH, CLUCK, CACKLE

23. CHIMPANZEE

Description: A chimpanzee is a primate that is covered in coarse black hair – except on its face, fingers, toes, palms and soles, all of which are bare.

Chimpanzee words: A chimpanzee, also known as a chimp, is a PAN TROGLODYTE. Some famous chimps are CHEETA (from the TARZAN films), NIM CHIMPSKI (who learned sign language), SARAH (who learned to form sentences using magnetic tokens) and more recently, LIMBANI, who lives in Miami and has an Instagram account.

Did you know? 1: Chimps display many signs of intelligence. They can learn and remember symbols, cooperate, use tools, and recognise themselves in a mirror.

Did you know? 2: Chimpanzees sometimes laugh when they play.

Did you know? 3: Like humans, chimps have opposable thumbs (thumbs that can be moved independently).

Collective noun possibilities: TROOP, WHOOP, FAMILY, CARTLOAD, COMMUNITY, APTITUDE, CLEVERNESS, AGILITY, QUICKNESS, PERSPICACITY, WIT

24. CLOWNFISH

Description: Clown fish are small, colourful, reef-dwelling fish. Their colours depend on the specific species, the most well-known being the ocellaris clownfish (like Nemo in 'Finding Nemo'), which is bright orange with white stripes and blackish-brown rims.

Clown fish words: Clown fish species include the ORANGE, TOMATO and PINK SKUNK CLOWNFISH. Clown fish are sometimes also known as CLOWN ANEMONE-FISH, as they form mutual symbiotic relationships with the multi-coloured sea anemone in the coral reefs where they live.

Did you know? 1: Male and female clownfish are dedicated parents.

Did you know? 2: All clownfish are born male, some changing to become the dominant female if required.

Did you know? 3: Clown fish are very sociable and make clicking and popping noises to communicate.

Collective noun possibilities: SCHOOL, CIRCUS, FESTIVAL, SPECTACLE

25. COCKROACH

Description: The cockroach has a flattish, oval-shaped body, long delicate antennae, and a shiny black or brown, leathery outer-protective layer. Its head faces downwards. Cockroaches are frequently depicted in art, literature and films etc. - usually as being vile and dirty.

Cockroach words: Cockroach species include the SMOKY-BROWN, MADAGASCAR HISSING, DEATH'S HEAD, DUSKY and FLORIDA WOODS COCKROACH. The Spanish word for cockroach is CUCARACHA, well known partly because of the famous song, 'La Cucaracha'.

Fun fact 1: Cockroaches are generally nocturnal and try to avoid the light.

Fun fact 2: A cockroach can live for up to a week without its head.

Fun fact 3: They prefer warm environments that are close to water and food, and dislike strong scents, such as peppermint and vinegar.

Collective noun possibilities: INTRUSION, FILTH, SQUALOR, IMPURITY, POLLUTION, UNCLEANLINESS, REPUGNANCE, SLEAZE

26. CORAL

Description: Although corals look like plants, they are technically animals as they don't make their own food like plants do. Instead, they use their thin, tentacle-like limbs to gather food from the water and to put it into their mouths.

Coral words: There are over 6,000 types of coral, including ELKHORN, OPEN BRAIN, BUBBLE, LEAF, VASE, VENUS SEA FAN, ORGAN PIPE, CLUBBED FINGER, SMOOTH CAULIFLOWER and COLOURFUL SEA WHIP.

Did you know? 1: A quarter of marine species live amongst coral reefs.

Did you know? 2: Corals clean the water that they live in.

Did you know? 3: The Great Barrier Reef is the largest coral reef in the world, an area of approximately 133,000 square miles.

Collective noun possibilities: REEF, BLOOM, EXPANSE, MYRIAD, PLENITUDE, BOUNTY, DIVERSITY, POT-POURRI, MEDLEY

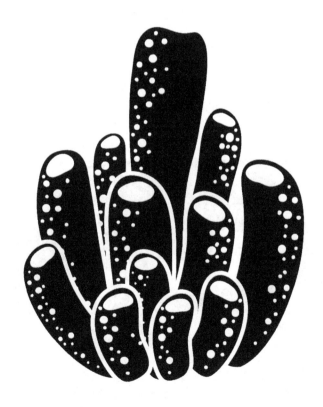

27. COW

Description: A cow is a large, domesticated animal with cloven-hooves, a rectangular-shaped body, a large udder, thin legs and tail, and a slow gait. These ruminant herbivores come in various different colours and are mainly farmed for either their beef or their milk.

Cow words: Cows generally fall into one of two main groups – INDICUS (those adapted to hot climates) and TAURINE (their cooler-climate cousins). Some taurine breeds are ABERDEEN ANGUS, HOLSTEIN, ENGLISH LONGHORN, JUTLAND and JERSEY. Some indicus breeds are RED CHITTAGONG, WHITE LAMPHUN, MASAI and MADAGASCAR ZEBU. HEIFERS and COWS are females and STEERS and BULLS are males. Young cows are CALVES. All cow-related animals are BOVINE.

Did you know? 1: Cows have long been important within a variety of human cultures. They are honoured as sacred creatures in the Hindu religion and are also part of the Chinese zodiac. In Spain and some other countries, bulls are sometimes bred for bullfighting and bull-riding.

Did you know? 2: The cow's large udder is a distinguishing feature. The vast quantity of milk that comes from cows provides the main source of milk, cheese and butter world-wide. Cow udders themselves used to be regularly eaten in a variety of cultures.

Did you know? 3: Cows' stomachs are made up of four different pouches.

Collective noun possibilities: CATTLE, HERD, DRIFT, DROVE, KINE, FLINK, RUMINATION, CONTEMPLATION, MEDITATION, PONDERING

28. CRAB

Description: Crabs are decapods (meaning they have ten legs). Most crabs are covered in a thick exoskeleton and have a strong pair of claws or pincers for catching and crushing prey.

Crab words: There are two types of crab: TRUE CRABS (with a short, well-protected abdomen) and FALSE CRABS (with a longer, less well-protected abdomen). Some false crabs are HORSESHOE CRABS (which have bright blue blood) as well as HERMIT and PORCELAIN CRABS. The smallest species of true crab is the PEA CRAB and the largest species is the JAPANESE SPIDER CRAB. The SALLY LIGHTFOOT CRAB is the most colourful crab in the world – red, orange, yellow and white.

Did you know? 1: Crabs have teeth in their stomachs. Atlantic ghost crabs use these teeth to make growling sounds to ward off predators.

Did you know? 2: Not all crabs move sideways. Some crabs are able to walk forwards and others can move in any direction.

Did you know? 3: If a crab loses a claw or leg, over time, it usually grows back again.

Collective noun possibilities: CAST, SCUTTLE, PINCH, NIP, GRASP, CLINCH, SNATCH

29. CRICKET

Description: A cricket is a small to medium-sized insect with a round head, long antennae, and a cylinder-shaped body. Crickets also have hind legs with large femora (thighs) to enable powerful jumping.

Cricket words: Cricket species include the GREAT GREEN BUSH-CRICKET, TROPICAL HOUSE CRICKET, SPECKLED BUSH-CRICKET, SHORT-WINGED CONEHEAD, and the WART-BITER.

Did you know? 1: Most male crickets create a chirping sound by scraping together areas of their wings that are specially textured.

Did you know? 2: Crickets are popular pets and considered to be good luck in some Asian countries.

Did you know? 3: It's very hard to sneak up on a cricket as they have tympanal organs (a bit like ears) on their legs that are highly sensitive, even to the slightest vibration.

Collective noun possibilities: CHIRP, JUMP, HOP, VAULT, HURDLE, SOMERSAULT, RICOCHET, FLICK, DART

30. CROCODILE

Description: Crocodiles are the largest reptiles on earth – with male saltwater crocodiles reaching up to 6 metres long. Crocodiles have a strong, muscular tail, powerful jaws, conical teeth and webbed feet with claws.

Crocodile words: Crocodile species include the NILE, MARSH, FRESHWATER, WEST-AFRICAN SLENDER-SNOUTED and DWARF CROCODILE. A male crocodile is a BULL, a female is a COW and baby crocodiles are HATCHLINGS.

Did you know? 1: Only a crocodile's eyes, nostrils and ears need to show above the water when it chooses to hide the majority of its scaly, leathery body beneath the surface.

Did you know? 2: Crocodiles don't chew their food.

Did you know? 3: 'Crocodile tears' means a false display of emotion to elicit sympathy from others. The idea comes from an ancient belief that crocodiles cry in order to lure their prey or that they weep for the victims they are consuming. Crocodiles do in fact 'cry', but it seems that this is to lubricate their eyes.

Collective noun possibilities: BASK, CONGREGATION, NEST, FLOAT, SNAP, SWALLOW, PRETENCE, GULP, GOBBLE, CHUGALUG, GUZZLE, RAVAGE, GORGE, VORACIOUSNESS

31. DODO

Description: Dodos were flightless birds that lived on the island of Mauritius. No complete specimen exists, so the exact colours of their feathers etc. isn't fully known. The dodo was thought to have a grey head, a green, black and yellow beak, and thick yellow legs with black claws.

Dodo words: The dodo's scientific name is RAPHUS CUCULLATUS.

Did you know? 1: Dodos were both discovered and became extinct within the very short space of a century – the last confirmed sighting being in 1662. It's thought that their becoming extinct is directly connected to how easy they were to catch.

Did you know? 2: The dodo's significance as one of the most well-known extinct creatures has led to it being portrayed in literature (e.g. in Alice in Wonderland) and it is often used as a metaphor for something now dead or obsolete.

Did you know? 3: The dodo's iconic shape is used to promote a variety of environmental organisations.

Collective noun possibilities: FLOCK, WADDLE, TODDLE, SHUFFLE

32. DOG

Description: A dog is a four-legged mammal and a domesticated descendant of the wolf. Dogs have sharp teeth and come in a number of very varied-looking breeds.

Dog words: Dog breeds include the BULLDOG, POODLE, BOXER, CHIHUAHUA, BORDER COLLIE, PUG, DOBERMANN, DACHSHUND, SIBERIAN HUSKY, BASSETT HOUND, GREAT DANE and LABRADOR RETRIEVER. Some hybrid dog breeds also have their own specific names: COCKAPOO, for example. Dogs are also known in familiar terms, like MUTT, POOCH and HOUND. LAIKA, a Soviet space dog, was the first ever animal to make an orbital space-flight around the Earth. The Latin for dog is CANIS FAMILIARIS. A young dog is a PUPPY.

Did you know? 1: Dogs and humans have developed a special bond and as a result, dogs are sometimes referred to as 'man's best friend'.

Did you know? 2: Culturally, dogs have symbolised faithfulness, loyalty, protection and guidance.

Did you know? 3: Dogs have a much better sense of smell than humans – up to forty times more sensitive.

Collective noun possibilities: PACK, KENNEL, LITTER. Also, GRUMBLE (pugs), TORNADO (Terriers), NIP (Corgis), HALO (Golden Retrievers), BOING (Springer Spaniels), AVALANCHE (St Bernards)

33. DOLPHIN

Description: Dolphins are marine mammals with streamlined bodies and fins. Their skin is smooth and rubbery, and colour-wise, they tend to be a mixture of black, white and grey.

Dolphin words: Dolphin species include the BOTTLENOSE, LONG-BEAKED COMMON, CHINESE WHITE, STRIPED, ROUGH-TOOTHED, DUSKY, HOURGLASS and MELON-HEADED DOLPHIN. The name 'dolphin' originates from the Greek word 'DELPHUS' meaning 'WOMB' – essentially, a fish with a womb. The French word for dolphin is DAUPHIN.

Did you know? 1: Dolphins are known for their high level of intelligence and playful behaviour.

Did you know? 2: They use a wide variety of sounds and gestures to communicate with each other. These include 'whistles' and 'clicks', slapping their tail and flippers on the water, leaping, bumping each other and spy hopping (popping just their head out of the water to look around).

Did you know? 3: Dolphins are known to blow bubbles in order to herd their prey to the surface.

Collective noun possibilities: POD, SUPERPOD, ALERTNESS, WISDOM, APTITUDE, IQ, INTELLECT, BRIGHTNESS, ENTERTAINMENT, FESTIVITY, FROLIC, JOLLITY

34. DONKEY

Description: A donkey is a large, four-legged, domesticated farm animal with hooves. All donkeys have a cross on their back, from the poll (between their ears) to the tip of their tail and down over their shoulders.

Donkey words: Types of donkey include the STANDARD, MINIATURE, MAMMOTH, POITOU, SPOTTED DONKEY and GRAND NOIR DU BERRY. A female donkey is known as a JENNY, and a male as a JACK. A MOKE is a British term for a donkey and BURRO is the word for donkey in Spanish. A baby donkey is called a FOAL.

Did you know? 1: Donkeys are almost as intelligent as dogs or dolphins. They have great memories for other donkeys and places they've been to. They also have a reputation for being stubborn, but this is at least partly because of their intelligence and their acute awareness of potential danger.

Did you know? 2: Donkeys are sometimes referred to as a 'beast of burden' – an animal employed to carry heavy loads. They are also symbols of service, suffering, peace and humility throughout the Bible.

Did you know? 3: Donkeys don't produce natural oils to make their coats waterproof.

Collective noun possibilities: DROVE, HARDSHIP, ENCUMBRANCE, SORROW, DUTY, RESIGNATION, OBEDIENCE, PATIENCE, SERENITY, FRIENDSHIP, LOYALTY, LOWLINESS

35. DOVE

Description: A dove is a smallish bird with a roundish body, a small head and short legs. Doves also have pointed beaks and long wing and tail feathers.

Dove words: Doves and pigeons come from the same family, doves being smaller and with a more fanned-out tail. Doves include the MOURNING, TURTLE and COLLARED DOVE. The WHITE DOVE (aka the SACRED WHITE DOVE) is a white mutation of the RING-NECK DOVE. A young dove is called a SQUAB.

Did you know? 1: Doves, as well as pigeons, were used for centuries to deliver messages during wars and to royalty.

Did you know? 2: Doves are a symbol of peace, gentleness and the divine Holy Spirit in the Christian faith – and they genuinely are peaceful, good-natured birds. A dove was the first bird to come back to Noah's ark after the great flood, said to be carrying an olive branch in its beak.

Did you know? 3: In Doric, a dialect spoken around the Aberdeen area of Scotland, asking, 'Foos yer doos?' to someone (literally, 'How are your doves?'), is one way of asking how a person is getting on. The ideal response would be, 'Aye peckin' awa, aye peckin' awa.' ('Always pecking away...').

Collective noun possibilities: COTE, BEVY, FLIGHT, PITYING, PRETENCE, PITEOUSNESS, PRETTYING, TENDERNESS, OUTPOURING, ALABASTER

36. DRAGON

Description: A dragon is a large, legendary, serpentine creature that is often depicted as having four legs, spikes, scales, wings and a tail. Some dragons are also described as having more than one head.

Dragons: Dragon legends exist in most cultural mythologies. Some of the more modern dragons are: SMAUG, TOOTHLESS and PUFF, THE MAGIC DRAGON. Some famous dragons of old include FAFNIR (from Scandinavia), VRITRA (from India), the AZURE DRAGON OF THE EAST (from China), as well as the dragon from the story of Saint George and the Dragon. Baby dragons are HATCHLINGS, WYRMLINGS or WHELPS. In Greek mythology, a DRAKAINA is a female dragon.

Did you know? 1: In China, emperors were believed to be the descendants of celestial dragons. This was considered very good, as dragons in China are thought of as benevolent, wise and powerful.

Did you know? 2: In the West, dragons have tended more to have the reputation of being powers of evil.

Did you know? 3: As well as being able to breathe fire and/or ice, some dragons also have extra superpowers. These include: changing size or form, being able to hide in water, an ability to blend in with their surroundings, and being able to glow in the dark.

Collective noun possibilities: BROOD, FLIGHT, THUNDER, WING, UPROAR, INFERNO, COMBUSTION, FLARE, SCORCH, POWERHOUSE, MIGHT, MALEVOLENCE, SAGE

37. DRAGONFLY

Description: A dragonfly is a flying insect with a long, thin body, two pairs of transparent (sometimes also coloured) wings, and two multifaceted, compound eyes. Many dragonflies are iridescent or metallic-looking.

Dragonfly words: Dragonfly species include the EMPEROR DRAGONFLY, SOUTHERN HAWKER, GOLDEN-RINGED DRAGONFLY, FOUR-SPOTTED CHASER and COMMON DARTER. Dragonflies also have nicknames in various different countries, such as DEVIL'S DARNING NEEDLE, EAR-CUTTER and EYE-POKER.

Did you know? 1: In many parts of the world, dragonflies symbolise change, transformation, adaptability and self-realisation.

Did you know? 2: Dragonflies have incredible flying abilities. Their wings have muscles that allow them to change the angle of each individual wing separately and therefore to fly with amazing precision.

Did you know? 3: Their huge compound eyes have 30,000 facets, each of which gives the dragonfly useful visual information. This helps them to easily pinpoint prey and to be very successful hunters.

Collective noun possibilities: FLIGHT, SWARM, CLUSTER, RADIANCE, OPALESCENCE, PRISM, FLASH, FLIT – although dragonflies do tend to be solitary

38. DUCK

Description: Ducks are similar but smaller birds than geese or swans and have shorter necks. They have a lozenge-shaped body, a rounded head, a flattish, rounded beak and three eyelids. Their waterproof feathers and webbed feet make them ideal swimmers.

Duck words: There are many duck species throughout the world, including the AYLESBURY, INDIAN RUNNER, MINIATURE SILVER APPLE-YARD, MUSCOVY DUCK, BLACK-BELLIED WHISTLING DUCK, COMMON EIDER DUCK, HARLEQUIN DUCK, TUFTED DUCK and MALLARD.

Males are DRAKES, females are DUCKS or HENS and the young are DUCKLINGS.

Did you know? 1: Ducks are known for being very caring and protective of their ducklings as well as for the way some species dabble in the water with their tails in the air.

Did you know? 2: Not all ducks quack. Some coo, some whistle, some yodel and others grunt.

Did you know? 3: Ducks sometimes eat gravel, small stones and sand, store them in their gizzards, and use their rough textures to help them digest food.

Collective noun possibilities: RAFT, PADDLING, WADDLING, BADLING, SKEIN, FLOCK, TEAM, BED, BRACE, BROOD, FLEET, FLUSH, PUDDLE

39. EAGLE

Description: Most eagles are bigger than other birds of prey. They have large hooked beaks, strong legs and powerful talons.

Eagle words: There are more than 60 species of eagle. The BALD EAGLE has been the national symbol of the USA since 1782. It isn't actually bald, however. 'BALDE' is an Old English word meaning white, and the bald eagle has white feathers on its head. The eagle with the largest wingspan is the WHITE-TAILED SEA-EAGLE (86 inches). Other eagles are the GOLDEN, SHORT-TOED SNAKE, HARPY, SPANISH IMPERIAL, PYGMY and ORNATE HAWK-EAGLE. Baby eagles are called EAGLETS.

Did you know? 1: Eagles are apex predators – at the top of their food chain.

Did you know? 2: Eagles mate for life.

Did you know? 3: The eagle is symbolic of a number of qualities including power, strength, courage, hope, divinity, and loyalty.

Collective noun possibilities: SOAR, CONVOCATION, ASCENSION, RISE, MAJESTY, ASPIRATION, OPTIMISM, AMBITION, AUDACITY, PLUCK, ALLEGIANCE

40. EEL

Description: Eels are ray-finned fish with long, slippery bodies that are covered in a slimy mucus. Freshwater eels are more cylinder-shaped than saltwater eels.

Eel words: There are around 800 eel species, including the RIBBON, SAWTOOTH, CUT-THROAT, ELECTRIC, PEACOCK, CONGER, FIRE and SPAGHETTI EEL. A baby eel is called an ELVER.

Did you know? 1: Some eels have over one hundred vertebrae.

Did you know? 2: Electric eels can create incredibly strong electric shocks. They store then release the power from specialised cells that are like mini batteries.

Did you know? 3: Eels can swim both backwards and forwards.

Collective noun possibilities: BED, OOZE, SLIP, SLITHER, STREAM, WRIGGLE, GLISSADE, SLINK

41. ELEPHANT

Description: Elephants are the largest land animals. Their uniqueness also lies in their long trunks, large flappy ears and tree-trunk-like legs. They have a thin tail with thick black hairs on the end, ivory tusks, and flat feet with toes (five toes on the front and four on the back).

Elephant words: There are just two species of elephant – AFRICAN ELEPHANTS, which have ears that are shaped like Africa, and ASIAN ELEPHANTS, with ears that are similar to the shape of India. In 'Winnie the Pooh' by A.A. Milne, the word HEFFALUMP is used instead of 'elephant'. Some well-known elephant characters are: JUMBO, DUMBO, BABAR and ELMER.

Did you know? 1: Elephants use their trunks for smelling, breathing, drinking, spraying themselves with water and mud, picking up tiny items (like a blade of grass), tearing branches off trees – and trumpeting!

Did you know? 2: Elephants are loyal, protective and nurturing to their family as well as being strong and determined. They are also highly intelligent with good memories and have complex feelings and emotions. Plus, they are one of the very few animal species that can recognise themselves in a mirror.

Did you know? 3: Metaphorically, they symbolise strength, good fortune, health and happiness. The 'elephant in the room' is a metaphor for an obvious but difficult-to-mention topic or question that no one discusses but that everyone is aware of.

Collective noun possibilities: HERD, PARADE, MEMORY, PROCLAMATION, HERALD, STEADINESS, CONTENTMENT, JUBILATION, DETERMINATION, REMEMBRANCE

42. FAIRY

Description: A fairy is a mythical, supernatural being, usually with magical qualities and a human-like diminutive form. Some fairies are depicted as having wings.

Fairies: FAIRY, FAIRIE or FAE is a general word for FAE FOLK, who originate from the folklore of various European cultures. There are lots of different types of fae folk, including BROWNIES, PIXIES, BANSHEES, LEPRECHAUNS, ELVES, DWARVES, DRYADS, KELPIES and BOGGARTS.

Did you know? 1: Fairies are sometimes said to be able to change to assume the guise of different animals. In Scotland, fairy women were thought to be able to change into deer.

Did you know? 2: Some fairies were considered to be kind, others not so. They were often blamed for ill health before modern medicine was available.

Did you know? 3: In the many myths and legends about fairies, one recurring theme is the need to ward them off by using charms. Some examples of these are: wearing clothes inside out, hanging up an iron horseshoe, and planting a rowan tree near the front door.

Collective noun possibilities: HERD, FROLIC, ENCHANTMENT, ALLUREMENT, FASCINATION, DINKINESS

43. FLAMINGO

Description: Flamingos are wading birds with distinctively bendy necks, yellow and black beaks, long legs, and (most commonly) pinkish feathers. Adult flamingos range in colour from light pink to almost bright red, depending partly on the level of beta-carotene that they consume – mainly from shrimps, snails and algae.

Flamingo words: There are six species of flamingo, covering a wide geographical span. These are the GREATER, LESSER, AMERICAN, CHILEAN, ANDEAN and JAMES'S FLAMINGO.

Did you know? 1: Named for their flaming, colourful plumage, flamingos symbolise beauty, pleasure and fun. And because they aren't born pink and can take years to develop a strong shade, they also symbolise potential and the need to nurture it.

Did you know? 2: As well as standing on one leg (like most wading birds), flamingos are filter feeders and therefore need to turn their heads upside down to eat.

Did you know? 3: Very rarely, due to a genetic condition, a flamingo will have black feathers.

Collective noun possibilities: FLAMBOYANCE, FLOURISH, PAGEANT, POMP, BLUSH, BLOOM

44. FOX

Description: Related to dogs, foxes are small/medium-sized mammals with pointy ears, a triangular snout, and a long, bushy tail.

Fox words: The most common breed of fox is the RED FOX, which is wide-spread throughout the world. Other species include the GREY, ARCTIC, BAT-EARED and SWIFT FOX. Some well-known fox characters are FOXY LOXY, BRE'R FOX, THE FANTASTIC MR. FOX, BASIL BRUSH, and FIONA FOX. Foxes also appear in well-known fables, like 'The Fox and the Grapes'. A female fox is a VIXEN. A male fox is a TOD or DOG FOX.

Did you know? 1: Foxes can make around forty different sounds, including a scream.

Did you know? 2: They behave more like cats than they do dogs – they're nocturnal, climb trees, use their whiskers to navigate, and can retract their claws.

Did you know? 3: Foxes have the reputation of being cunning and sly.

Collective noun possibilities: SKULK, CHANCERY, CRAFTINESS, SUBTERFUGE, RUSE, TRICK, CONSPIRACY, DECEPTION, ILLUSION, DOUBLE-DEALING, PLOT, SKULDUGGERY

45. FROG

Description: Frogs are amphibians. They have bulbous eyes, a long, slit mouth, strong webbed hind feet for jumping and swimming, and smooth, moist skin.

Frog words: There are several thousand species of frog, including the POISON DART, RED-EYED TREE, ARGENTINE HORNED, AFRICAN CLAWED, AMERICAN BULLFROG, SMOKY JUNGLE, WALLACE'S FLYING, HAIRY, VIETNAMESE MOSSY and DESERT RAIN FROG.

Did you know? 1: Rather than drinking water through its mouth, a frog absorbs it through an area of skin called the drinking patch.

Did you know? 2: Many male frogs (and some females) have vocal sacs – pouches of skin that they inflate then use to create sounds with. Each frog's call is unique to its species.

Did you know? 3: A frog's tongue is attached to the front rather than to the back of its mouth. This allows frogs to stick their tongue out further in order to catch insects, etc.

Collective noun possibilities: ARMY, COLONY, BAND, CHORUS, BUNDLE, TROOP, BEVY, LEAP, HURDLE, VAULT, SPRING

46. GECKO

Description: Geckos are carnivorous lizards and are mostly small and nocturnal. They have soft skin, a shortish body, a tail, a large head and strong limbs.

Gecko words: The word 'gecko' comes from a similar Indonesian-Malay word and is onomatopoeic with regard to the sound that some geckos make. Known for their vocalisations, which vary according to species, geckos include the FLAME-CRESTED, GARGOYLE, LEOPARD and TANGERINE ALBINO AFRICAN FAT-TAILED GECKO.

Did you know? 1: Most geckos lack moveable eyelids. Because they therefore can't blink, they moisten and clean their eyes with their tongue.

Did you know? 2: Many species have specialised toe pads, which allow them to climb up walls and along ceilings.

Did you know? 3: Fat is stored in a gecko's tail, which it can use if needed, and a gecko can also shed its tail if it is grabbed by a predator. Fortunately, they can usually regrow their tail within 30 days.

Collective noun possibilities: CLAMBER, CLING – although geckos don't tend to form groups

47. GIANT

Description: Giants are mythological human-like beings but on a grander scale. Their size and strength are mainly what set them apart.

Giants: In some tales, giants are violent and unintelligent. In other stories, they are portrayed as both clever and friendly. Some famous giants from mythology/folklore around the world are: ATLAS, CRONUS, ORION, GOGMAGOG, ONI, POLYPHEMUS and BALOR.

Did you know? 1: In Greek mythology, Atlas was the giant who was condemned to hold up the sky for all eternity.

Did you know? 2: In Japanese folklore, Oni are incredibly strong giants with red or blue skin and grotesque horns.

Did you know? 3: Gogmagog was said to have been the very last giant in Britain - a rough, strong giant who could uproot trees.

Collective noun possibilities: PERCUSSION, IMMENSITY, TOWERING, MAGNITUDE, ENORMITY

48. GIANT PANDA

Description: Giant pandas are bears with a distinctive black and white coat and a roundish body.

Panda words: The giant panda and the red panda are unrelated. The word 'panda' is thought to come from the Nepali word 'PONYA', meaning 'BAMBOO EATER' or 'BAMBOO FOOTED' – and both pandas do eat bamboo – up to 12kg of bamboo a day in the case of a giant panda.

Did you know? 1: Giant pandas can swim and climb trees.

Did you know? 2: They are the ultimate introverts, preferring to only meet up in order to mate – although, baby pandas do stay with their mother until they are about 18 months old.

Did you know? 3: Giant pandas have six fingers.

Collective noun possibilities: EMBARRASSMENT, SOUL-SEARCHING, REFLECTION, WONDER

49. GIRAFFE

Description: Giraffes are the tallest animals on Earth. They have very long necks and legs, their legs alone being around 6 feet in length. They have patterned, browny-orange and white coats and small, hair-covered horns called ossicones.

Giraffe words: The four species of giraffe are the MASAI, NORTHERN, SOUTHERN and RETICULATED GIRAFFE. There are also several subspecies. In Afrikaans, the word for a giraffe is KAMEELPERD ('CAMEL-LEOPARD').

Did you know? 1: Giraffes have a very long, blue-black or purple tongue.

Did you know? 2: Because their necks aren't able to reach the ground, giraffes have to bend down into an awkward position (making themselves vulnerable to predators) to be able to drink at a water hole.

Did you know? 3: Adult giraffes are generally quiet but are known to snort and hiss – and sometimes to make a humming noise when sleeping. Giraffes also make infrasonic sounds that humans can only hear using specialized equipment. Young giraffes sometimes 'moo', especially if stressed.

Collective noun possibilities: TOWER, ELEVATION, SUMMIT, APEX

50. GNOME

Description: Gnomes originated in Scandinavian folklore as house gnomes. They are legendary, small-in-stature humanoids that are sometimes described as shrivelled, little old men with pointy, red hats and long beards. Male gnomes are often portrayed as wearing boots and females as wearing pointed clogs.

Gnome words: A gnome is often known as TOMTE (in Sweden), NISSER (in Norway) and TONTTU (in Finland). Gnomes tend to stay behind the scenes, but from time to time, a notable gnome emerges. Some modern gnomes include: GNORMAN (the policeman gnome), THE ROAMING GNOME (who travels the world), HOWARD (the world's tallest gnome) and FRANKIE (the chrome gnome).

Did you know? 1: The character, abilities and purposes of gnomes can vary, depending on where they come from. Gnomes are often said to protect farmsteads, crops, animals and children, but also have a reputation for mischievous pranks and behaviour. They are sometimes thought to live underground, guarding the Earth's buried treasures.

Did you know? 2: Most gnomes don't seem to like change.

Did you know? 3: Gnomes are considered by some to be symbols of good luck, and gnome statues are still sometimes placed in gardens or hidden in the rafters of barns, often with that in mind.

Collective noun possibilities: LAWN, RAFTER, WRINKLE, WITHER, WIZEN

51. GOAT

Description: Related to sheep but more lightly built, goats are ruminant mammals with hollow, backward-facing horns. Goats also have rectangular-shaped pupils and male goats tend to have a beard.

Goat words: They are usually kept for their milk, meat or fleece and include the ALPINE, ANGORA, BARBARI, NIGERIAN DWARF and PYGMY GOAT. A female goat is called a NANNY/DOE, a male is a BILLY/BUCK and a baby goat is a KID.

Did you know? 1: No kidding, when a goat gives birth, it's called 'kidding'.

Did you know? 2: Goats are very intelligent and curious and love to explore their environment.

Did you know? 3: Goats are good climbers and some even climb trees.

Collective noun possibilities: TRIP, TRIBE, MEDDLING, SNOOP, PRY, AGILITY, CLAMBER

52. GOLDFISH

Description: Common goldfish come in a number of colours. As well as the widely-known orange/yellow variety, there are also red, blueish-grey, brown, yellow and white/black goldfish. They come with two sets of paired fins (pectoral and pelvic) as well as three single fins. They don't have scales on their head.

Goldfish words: Goldfish species include the COMMON, COMET, SHUBUNKIN, NYMPH, PEARL-SCALE, FANTAIL, POMPOM, CELESTIAL EYE, TELESCOPE and TRI-COLOUR BUBBLE EYES GOLDFISH. Goldfish also have a variety of tail types, including WILD, COMET-TAILED, HEART-SHAPED, FAN-TAILED, RIBBON-TAILED and BUTTERFLY-TAILED.

Did you know? 1: Goldfish can survive in very low temperatures, even under a frozen-over pond.

Did you know? 2: It's a myth that goldfish only have a memory of a few seconds. In fact, the memory span of goldfish can last at least three months.

Did you know? 3: Goldfish can grow to over a foot long if they're kept in the right environment.

Collective noun possibilities: GLINT, TROUBLING

53. GOOSE

Description: A goose is a large waterfowl bird with webbed feet and a longer neck than a duck.

Goose words: The CANADA GOOSE is the largest breed of goose in the world. Other geese include the GREYLAG, SNOW, BARNACLE and PINK-FOOTED GOOSE. The female is a GOOSE, the male is a GANDER and young geese are GOSLINGS.

Did you know? 1: Migratory geese fly in a v-shaped formation to conserve their energy as they have less wind resistance that way.

Did you know? 2: Geese often make a honking sound while they fly.

Did you know? 3: There are lots of well-known sayings about geese. To 'have a gander' is to look at something; to say that someone's 'goose is cooked' means the person has had or will have something go wrong, and going on a 'wild goose chase' means doing something that leads nowhere. If someone calls you a 'silly goose', it's an insult of sorts, but a very mild one.

Collective noun possibilities: GAGGLE, SKEIN, PLUMP

54. GORILLA

Description: Gorillas are the largest living primates, with some reaching almost 2m in height. They have a broad chest and shoulders, a stocky physique, hands like humans, and a hairless face.

Gorilla words: There are two species of gorilla in the world, each with two subspecies. EASTERN GORILLAS consist of the MOUNTAIN GORILLA and the EASTERN LOWLAND GORILLA, and WESTERN GORILLAS consist of the CROSS RIVER GORILLA and the WESTERN LOWLAND GORILLA. Adult male gorillas from around 12 years old are known as SILVERBACKS because of the grey/white hair they then have on their backs.

Did you know? 1: Gorillas partly move around by knuckle-walking.

Did you know? 2: They are known for their formidable strength and can lift things that are ten times their body weight.

Did you know? 3: Gorillas sometimes beat their chests, either as part of a ritual to intimidate potential rivals without becoming physical, or to attract females.

Collective noun possibilities: TROOP

55. GRIFFIN

Description: A griffin is a legendary, lion-eagle hybrid from Egyptian, Mesopotamian, Persian, Minoan, Greek and Roman mythologies. Griffins are generally shown to have the body, tail and back legs of a lion and the head and wings of an eagle. The Asiatic griffin is said to have a crested head. The Greek and Minoan griffins are often depicted with a mane of spiral-shaped curls.

Griffin words: GRIFFON and GRYPHON are alternative spellings.

Did you know? 1: Because the lion is thought of as king of the beasts and the eagle as top bird, the griffin is considered particularly powerful and majestic, both royal and divine – and as ruling over all creatures.

Did you know? 2: A griffin's superpowers are incredible strength, sight and flight.

Did you know? 3: Its weakness is fire, especially having its wings set on fire.

Collective noun possibilities: DRIFT, WING, FLIGHT, PRIDE, CONVOCATION

56. GRIZZLY BEAR

Description: Grizzly bears are large bears that range in colour from dark brown to cream. They have short, rounded ears and a large shoulder hump. The claws of a grizzly bear can be up to four inches long.

Grizzly bear words: The MAINLAND GRIZZLY BEAR – URSUS ARCTOS HORRIBILIS – is sometimes also known as the NORTH AMERICAN BROWN BEAR. The KODIAK BEAR is the largest subspecies of grizzly bear. Other subspecies include the CALIFORNIAN GRIZZLY BEAR and the MEXICAN GRIZZLY BEAR, both of which are sadly now presumed extinct. Grizzly bear/polar bear hybrids occur very occasionally and are referred to as GROLAR or PIZZLY BEARS.

Did you know? 1: Grizzly bears go into a mild state of hibernation called a torpor in the winter months.

Did you know? 2: The hump on the back of grizzly bears' shoulders is a large muscle that they use to add power to their forelimbs.

Did you know? 3: Grizzlies have some useful abilities, including a very keen sense of smell – they can detect food from great distances – and being fast runners and capable swimmers.

Collective noun possibilities: SLEUTH

57. HEDGEHOG

Description: Hedgehogs are small mammals with thin legs, a pointy snout, and between 5000 and 7000 spines/quills on their back. They have grey-brown fur on the rest of their body.

Hedgehog words: There are 17 species of hedgehog, including the FOUR-TOED, LONG-EARED, DESERT and the BARE-BELLIED HEDGEHOG. Hedgehogs used to be called URCHINS. Baby hedgehogs are called HOGLETS. Some famous hedgehogs are: MRS TIGGY WINKLE (from Beatrix Potter's stories), PINNY NEEDLEKIN (in Racey Helps' books) and SONIC THE HEDGEHOG (who appears in a number of video games).

Did you know? 1: Hedgehogs curl up into a spiny ball when they feel threatened.

Did you know? 2: They eat beetles, caterpillars and earthworms as well as small mice, frogs, eggs and snakes. They also tend to be noisy eaters.

Did you know? 3: Hedgehogs are nocturnal, mainly solitary, and also lactose intolerant.

Collective noun possibilities: ARRAY, PRICKLE, SPIKE

58. HIPPOPOTAMUS

Description: Hippos are very large, rotund, semiaquatic mammals. As well as having a bulky body, they also have short, stumpy legs, an enormous head, and a thin, short tail.

Hippo words: The two hippo species are the COMMON RIVER HIPPO and the PYGMY HIPPO. The word 'hippopotamus' comes from the Greek for 'RIVER HORSE'. They spend a lot of their time in the river to keep their skin cool and moist, but they aren't related to horses in any way.

Did you know? 1: Hippos are very loud. However, as well as snorts, grunts, bellows, grumbles and wheeze-honks, they also use subsonic vocalisations to communicate.

Did you know? 2: Hippos are aggressive, dangerous animals who use their tusks and teeth to attack.

Did you know? 3: They are mainly herbivorous.

Collective noun possibilities: BLOAT, POD, SIEGE

59. HOBBIT

Description: Hobbits are fictional humanoids who were created by J. R. R. Tolkien for his books 'The Hobbit' and the 'Lord of the Rings' trilogy. Hobbits are about half the size of an average human and have leathery feet (no need for shoes) and curly hair. Proudfoot hobbits have larger than average feet.

Hobbit words: Tolkien also created a fictional ancestry for the hobbits. HARFOOTS, FALLOHIDES and STOORS are three different types of hobbit, each one differing in both physical traits and temperament. Some significant hobbits from the books are BILBO BAGGINS, FRODO BAGGINS, PIPKIN TOOK, MERRY BRANDYBUCK and SAM GAMGEE. Hobbits are occasionally referred to as HALFLINGS.

Did you know? 1: Bilbo is the main protagonist in 'The Hobbit' and his development can be seen to represent the inner latent heroism that we all have.

Did you know? 2: Hobbits love to eat and socialise, and it's in their nature to enjoy the simple pleasures of life – such as breakfast, second breakfast, elevenses, luncheon, afternoon tea, dinner and supper.

Did you know? 3: Hobbits are depicted as home-loving and unadventurous, although they do occasionally get involved in adventures.

Collective noun possibilities: FELLOWSHIP

60. HORSE

Description: A horse is a hoofed mammal with a flowing mane and tail. Horses also have short hair on their bodies, come in a variety of colours, and have long, slender legs, a thick neck, and a large, elongated head.

Horse words: Horse breeds include the ARAB, AMERICAN PAINT, BOSNIAN MOUNTAIN, CASPIAN, CLYDESDALE, IRISH DRAUGHT, MUSTANG, SWISS WARMBLOOD and THOROUGHBRED. Horses can also be described according to their different colour/s, such as CHESTNUT, BAY, BUCKSKIN, LEOPARD, PINTO, PIEBALD, SKEWBALD, DUN, CHAMPAGNE, PEARL, and PALOMINO. The word 'EQUINE' refers to any member of the horse family. Some famous horses from literature/television are: BLACK BEAUTY, BOXER, MOLLIE, CLOVER and TRIGGER. Famous race horses include RED RUM, SECRETARIAT, SEA BISCUIT and SHERGAR. Some other horse words are NAG, NEIGH and NICKER.

Did you know? 1: Horses can sleep either standing up or lying down.

Did you know? 2: They use their ears, eyes, nostrils and tail to express their feelings.

Did you know? 3: Most horses have four gaits: walk, trot, canter and gallop. The Icelandic horse has five!

Collective noun possibilities: TEAM, STUD, STABLE, HERD, PACK, TROOP, CLIP-CLOP, PRANCE

61. HUMMINGBIRD

Hummingbird words: Hummingbirds get their name from the noise their beating wings make. The fastest recorded rate is about 80 beats per second – by the AMETHYST WOOD-STAR HUMMINGBIRD. Other hummingbirds are the RUBY-THROATED, BLACK-CHINNED, COSTA'S, BUFF-BELLIED and the VIOLET-CROWNED HUMMINGBIRD – as well as the smallest one of all, the BEE HUMMINGBIRD.

Did you know? 1: When food is scarce, hummingbirds can become fatigued and go into a torpor (a light hibernation-like state).

Did you know? 2: Hummingbirds can fly like a helicopter – forwards, backwards, up, down, left and right.

Did you know? 3: The hummingbird's long beak is a protective sheath for its forked tongue, which is covered in tiny hairs – a perfectly combined tool for extracting nectar from flowers.

Collective noun possibilities: CHARM, BOUQUET, GLITTERING, SHIMMER, POSY, GARLAND

62. JELLYFISH

Description: A jellyfish has a bell and most also have tentacles. The bell pulsates to create movement and the tentacles contain stinging cells, which are used for both attack and defence. Some jellyfish are bioluminescent (they glow in the dark).

Jellyfish words: The size and colour of jellyfish varies greatly and includes the MOON JELLY, LION'S MANE JELLYFISH, BARREL JELLYFISH (aka the DUST-BIN LID or FRILLY-MOUTHED JELLYFISH), the CANNONBALL JELLYFISH (aka the CABBAGE-HEAD JELLYFISH) and the HELMET JELLYFISH. Jellyfish are sometimes referred to as SEA JELLIES.

Did you know? 1: The effect of a jellyfish sting ranges from mild discomfort to death, depending on the species of jellyfish. Box jellyfish should definitely be avoided!

Did you know? 2: Jellyfish have no blood, no brain, no heart and no bones. About 95% of a jellyfish is water. The remaining 5% is made up of three layers: the outer later (epidermis), the middle layer (a jelly-like material called mesoglea) and an inner layer (gastrodermis).

Did you know? 3: One species of jellyfish – Turritopsis dohnii – has been called biologically immortal. These sea jellies have the ability to revert to an earlier stage of their life cycle.

Collective noun possibilities: SMACK

63. KANGAROO

Description: Kangaroos are large, brown, grey or red marsupials with very strong back legs. Their large feet also make them macropods. Kangaroos have muscular tails, short front paws, long, pointed ears and a small head. The pouch on the front of female kangaroos is called a marsupium.

Kangaroo words: The EASTERN GREY, RED, ANTILOPINE and the WESTERN GREY are the four species of kangaroo. WALLABIES are also members of the clan. There are various slang words for kangaroos in Australia: Males can be BUCKS, BOOMERS or JACKS, and females DOES, FLYERS or JILLS. A baby kangaroo is called a JOEY. 'ROO' is a shortened version of kangaroo and 'SKIPPY', a word originating from a 1960's TV show, refers to any kangaroo.

Did you know? 1: Kangaroos love to hop, and some adult kangaroos can jump over 9 metres in a single bound.

Did you know? 2: A joey will stay in its mother's pouch for about 6-8 months before venturing out for short periods of time.

Did you know? 3: Most kangaroos are left-handed.

Collective noun possibilities: MOB, TROOP, COURT, BOUNCE, BOING

64. KINGFISHER

Description: The common kingfisher is a small bird with easily recognisable plumage: its back and head are bright blue and it has an orange breast. Common kingfishers also have a long, black beak with a red area at the base if female.

Kingfisher words: There are nearly 90 species of kingfisher, including the GIANT, SACRED, ORIENTAL DWARF, BLUE-EARED, CRESTED and BROWN-HOODED KINGFISHER. The LAUGHING KOOKABURRA is the largest member of the kingfisher family.

Did you know? 1: The common kingfisher doesn't have a song, although it does have a shrill-sounding whistle.

Did you know? 2: Common kingfishers are renowned for having messy, unclean nests that are often strewn with fish bones and droppings.

Did you know? 3: The common kingfisher spends most of its time near rivers as this is where it finds fish to eat and creates its nest. However, there are many kingfisher species that don't eat fish and rarely go near water.

Collective noun possibilities: CONCENTRATION, CLIQUE, CROWN, REALM, RATTLE

65. KOALA

Description: Koalas are arboreal, herbivorous marsupials. They have a large, round head and grey/brown fur as well as a cream-coloured chest and inner arms. They also have a large, black nose, extra furry ears and strong paws with two thumbs on each hand. Their long claws are great for gripping and climbing.

Koala words: There's only one species of koala and possibly two or three subspecies. It's incorrect to call them 'koala bears'. Baby koalas are called JOEYS. The name 'koala' comes from an Aboriginal word and means 'NO DRINK' or 'NO WATER', which makes sense as they get most of their liquid through their food and are rarely seen to drink.

Did you know? 1: Koalas mainly eat eucalyptus leaves and are somewhat selective about which particular leaves they're prepared to consume, sometimes climbing to the very top of a tree to find the best ones.

Did you know? 2: Koalas usually sleep for at least 18 hours a day in the branches of a tree.

Did you know? 3: Most koalas smell like cough sweets. Older males, however, usually smell quite musky and pungent.

Collective noun possibilities: CLING, CLASP, FASTENING, EMBRACE, GRIP, HUG – although they are mainly solitary creatures

66. LADYBIRD/LADYBUG

Description: Ladybirds are a type of beetle. They have six short legs and most have an oval body. They can also be a variety of different colours (red, black, orange, metallic blue...) and patterns (spots, stripes, squiggles...). One of the most common ladybirds in Europe is red with 7 black spots.

Ladybird words: Ladybird species include the ASIAN LADY BEETLE, STEEL-BLUE LADYBIRD and HARMONIA CONFORMIS, as well as the 2, 11 and 18-SPOTTED LADYBIRDS. LADYBIRDS (UK) / LADYBUGS (US) are also sometimes called MARY'S BEETLES, LADY CLOCKS, GOD'S COWS, LADY FLIES and the LORD'S SWEET LITTLE CREATURES.

Did you know? 1: When feeling threatened, ladybirds can secrete a small amount of yellow liquid (their blood) from their legs.

Did you know? 2: Ladybugs have a pair of long, transparent flying wings under their hard protective wing cases.

Did you know? 3: In some countries, it's thought to be unlucky to kill a ladybird.

Collective noun possibilities: BLOOM, SPOT, LOVELINESS

67. LEOPARD

Description: Leopards are large, powerful, carnivorous mammals with long bodies, relatively short legs and a broad head. The various species all have dark, irregular spots (rosettes) on their coats – even black leopards, although their rosettes are only visible under infrared light.

Leopard words: There are a number of subspecies of leopard, including the AMUR, ARABIAN, JAVAN, AFRICAN and INDIAN LEOPARD. 'BLACK PANTHER' is the name used for a black variant of either a leopard or a jaguar.

Did you know? 1: Leopards like to climb trees and often drag their kill up high into a tree to prevent other animals from stealing it.

Did you know? 2: They are symbols of strength, agility, stealth, elusiveness, self-reliance and rare beauty.

Did you know? 3: Leopards are considered to be the strongest of all the big cats.

Collective noun possibilities: LEAP, SNARL

68. LION

Description: Lions are strong, yellow-gold big cats with a long body and a large head. Their legs are short in comparison. The males also have a shaggy mane and both males and females have a thin tail with a black tassel at the end.

Lion words: There are several subspecies of PANTHERA LEO (lion), including the WEST AFRICAN, CONGO, ASIATIC and NUBIAN LION. Lions are sometimes referred to as the 'KING OF THE JUNGLE'. Some famous lions are SIMBA (Swahili for 'lion'), ASLAN, KIMBA, SCARFACE and ELSA.

Did you know? 1: Female lions do most of the hunting, but the males eat first.

Did you know? 2: Lions are apex predators and also symbols of strength, power, ferocity, royalty, confidence and charisma.

Did you know? 3: Lions love to sleep – sometimes up to 20 hours a day.

Collective noun possibilities: PRIDE, COALITION, SOWSE, SAULT, TROOP, STREAK

69. LIZARD

Description: Lizards are typically scaly or spiny-skinned reptiles, usually with legs, external ear openings, and movable eyelids. They are almost all cold-blooded and about 90% of lizards lay eggs.

Lizard words: There are many different types of lizard, including GLASS and MONITOR LIZARDS, GECKOS, IGUANAS and SKINKS.

Did you know? 1: Some specific lizards have interesting and unusual abilities. The North American horned lizard can squirt blood from its eyes. The basilisk lizard can run on water.

Did you know? 2: Lizards vary as to how they keep hydrated and some can live their entire lives without drinking at all.

Did you know? 3: Some lizards can change colour. This may be to attract a mate, reflect their mood, or to adjust to the heat and/or light in their environment.

Collective noun possibilities: LOUNGE

70. LLAMA

Description: Llamas are long-necked camelids (related to camels, but in their case without any humps). They have a face and a split upper lip similar to a camel. They also have two-toed feet with a broad, leathery pad on the base – ideal for diverse terrains. Llamas' very thick fur can be various solid or spotted colours, including black, grey, brown, white and beige. They are about twice as big as alpacas, have much longer ears, and can grow up to 6 feet tall.

Llama words: Llama species include the CLASSIC, WOOLLY and SURI LLAMA. Scientifically speaking, a llama is a LAMA GLAMA. A baby llama is a CRIA.

Did you know? 1: Domesticated by the Incas, llamas are pack animals – but they also have their limits. Loading too much weight onto a llama may result in it lying down or refusing to walk.

Did you know? 2: Although smart and easy to train, llamas sometimes spit when annoyed.

Did you know? 3: Llama fleece is warm, light-weight, water-resistant and lanolin-free.

Collective noun possibilities: HERD

71. LOBSTER

Description: Lobsters are large marine crustaceans with long bodies and muscular tails. They have 5 pairs of legs and two different claw types – a larger crusher claw (to break up shells etc.) and a smaller pincher claw (to tear softer food). Most lobsters are brown, but they can also be orange, blue, blue-green, green-brown and more...

Lobster words: Lobsters have names that refer to their size. SHORTS or SNAPPERS are the smallest, right up to JUMBOS, which weigh over 2.5 pounds.

Did you know? 1: A lobster can cut off one of its limbs if required. Fortunately, they can also regenerate their limbs.

Did you know? 2: Lobsters have blue blood. This is due to copper-based haemocyanin, rather than iron-based haemoglobin in their blood, which carries the oxygen they need.

Did you know? 3: Lobsters keep on growing for as long as they can regenerate new shells to house their bigger bodies.

Collective noun possibilities: POD, RISK, GRASP, NIP, GRAPPLE, PINCE

72. LOCH NESS MONSTER

Description: The Loch Ness Monster is described as a large, long-necked animal with one or more humps that protrude from the water.

The story of the Loch Ness Monster: The Loch Ness Monster (aka NESSIE) is a creature from Scottish folklore, believed by some to continue to live in Loch Ness, a large freshwater lake in the Scottish Highlands. Nessie was brought to worldwide attention in 1933 when a local couple claimed to have seen 'an enormous animal rolling and plunging on the surface' [of the water] - like a 'dragon or prehistoric monster'. Interest grew and there was also a photograph (since discredited) of what looked like a brontosaurus-type dinosaur or enormous eel. Alleged footprints, sightings, and a variety of hoaxes have since surrounded the mystery.

Did you know? 1: The earliest written reference to a possible monster in the loch is from a 7th century biography of St Columba. Nessie scholars have also found various other references to a monster in Loch Ness, the earliest dating back to 500 A.D. - a Pictish carving found on a standing stone near to the loch.

Did you know? 2: The water of Loch Ness itself is very dark, as the rain carries peat from the nearby hills into it, making visibility very poor. A perfect place for a monster to hide in, perhaps...

Did you know? 3: No credible evidence of Nessie's existence has ever been found – so far!

Collective noun possibilities: LONELINESS, SOLITUDE, FORLORNNESS, REMOTENESS – although there is thought to be only one Loch Ness Monster

73. MANTA RAY

Description: Manta rays are fish with a large, diamond-shaped body and two wing-like pectoral fins. They also have a short, whip-like tail.

Manta ray words: Manta rays include the GIANT OCEANIC MANTA RAY, REEF MANTA RAY and the DEVIL FISH or GIANT DEVIL RAY. 'Manta' is Spanish for 'BLANKET' or 'CLOAK'.

Did you know? 1: A full-grown giant oceanic manta ray can reach up to 7 metres wide and weigh up to 2 tonnes.

Did you know? 2: Manta rays, unlike sting rays, are totally harmless to humans.

Did you know? 3: Mantas like to keep clean and they regularly visit areas where certain fish will nibble dead skin and parasites from their bodies.

Collective noun possibilities: FEVER, QUILT, BEDSPREAD, COUNTERPANE, PATCHWORK

74. MEERKAT

Description: Slim, with a pointy face and tiny little ears, the meerkat is a small, burrowing member of the mongoose family. Meerkats are sandy to light brown in colour and have dark stripes on their backs. They often give the impression that they are smiling wryly.

Meerkat words: There are three subspecies of meerkat – SURICATES, SLENDER-TAILED MEERKATS and GREY MEERKATS. Part of the meerkats' uniqueness lies in their trademark upright position, known as 'SENTINEL', where they look like they're on sentry duty.

Did you know? 1: They are gentle, sensitive and timid – and love to hug each other.

Did you know? 2: Meerkats have been found to be highly intelligent.

Did you know? 3: The dark patches around their eyes help them to be good lookouts as these areas reduce the glare from the sun.

Collective noun possibilities: MOB, GANG, PANORAMA, VIGILANCE, WATCHFULNESS, OBSERVANCE

75. MERMAID/MERMAN

Description: Mermaids/mermen are legendary hybrid creatures with the upper body of a human female/male and the tail of a fish.

Mermaid words: Merfolk (particularly mermaids) appear in stories in many cultures throughout the world. Some well-known mermaids are SYRENKA (aka THE MERMAID OF WARSAW), the STARBUCKS MERMAID, MAKO MERMAIDS, the WEEKI WACHEE MERMAIDS and Hans Christian Anderson's 'THE LITTLE MERMAID'. MERMAIDS, SEA NYMPHS, SIRENS and NIXIES all have similarities but also significant differences, and there has been much confusion throughout the years, especially between mermaids and sirens.

Did you know? 1: There have been many historical accounts of people seeing mermaids (e.g. Christopher Columbus when exploring the Caribbean). It is thought that these were probably sightings of manatees – although stories of mermaids being sighted still occur today...

Did you know? 2: Merpeople are often said to have various superpowers, depending on the particular mermaid/merman. Some of the more modern superpowers are: hydrokinesis, hydro-thermokinesis, aerokinesis and cryokinesis. Other abilities include extra fast swimming, shape-shifting, being able to turn invisible, being able to make their physical appearance more appealing, and being able to sing in such a way as to lure all who hear the singing towards the singer – although, that particular ability is more often attributed to sirens.

Did you know? 3: In many cultures, mermaids are mainly seen as positive symbols, suggesting happy times ahead. They represent independence, individuality, awareness, insight, renewal and being playful.

Collective noun possibilities: POD, SPLASH, TRIBE, SCHOOL, SHIMMER, FROLIC

76. MINOTAUR

Description: A minotaur is a hybrid creature, usually with a man's body and the head and tail of a bull.

Minotaur stories: The original Minotaur was a Greek mythological creature who was said to have lived in the centre of the Labyrinth, a complex maze within the Palace of Knossos on Crete. This original Minotaur was known as ASTERION. The story goes that the Minotaur was eventually killed by the Athenian hero Theseus. The use of 'minotaur' as a common noun, refers to similar creatures which have since appeared much later on, often in fantasy fiction.

Did you know? 1: Some versions show a man's head and torso on a bull's body.

Did you know? 2: The Minotaur was a savage, unintelligent creature with superhuman strength.

Did you know? 3: According to legend, the Minotaur needed to eat human beings to survive. Every few years, 7 young Athenian men and 7 Athenian maidens would be sent into the Labyrinth as a feast for the Minotaur. Theseus was one of these young men.

Collective noun possibilities: SNARL, MAZE

77. MOLE

Description: Moles are small mammals with roundish bodies, velvety fur and tiny eyes (often with quite limited vision). They also have a hairless, pointed snout as well as powerful forearms and wide paws that are ideal for digging. They don't always have external ears.

Mole words: There are 42 species of TRUE MOLES, including the HAIRY-TAILED, SHORT-FACED and STAR-NOSED MOLE – as well as several GOLDEN MOLES. The star-nosed mole has a touch organ (the star on its nose) with over 25,000 tiny sensory receptors, which help it find its way around.

Did you know? 1: Moles mainly live underground and are excellent at aerating the soil. Their tunnels also improve soil drainage, which in turn helps to prevent flooding.

Did you know? 2: A mole can dig up to 20 metres of tunnel in a single day.

Did you know? 3: Many mole species have a strong odour.

Collective noun possibilities: LABOUR

78. MOOSE

Description: A moose is a large ungulate (hoofed mammal), and the largest, heaviest member of the deer family. Moose have long, rounded snouts, a humped back and thin legs. Their huge, flattened antlers can be almost six feet wide, tip to tip. Both males and females have an area of skin called a bell that hangs down under their throat.

Moose words: EURASIAN ELK is another name for a moose. Their antlers are also known as PADDLES.

Did you know? 1: Moose have a huge appetite and enjoy browsing on shrubs, woody vegetation, aquatic plants, and buds throughout the day.

Did you know? 2: Although they do use their antlers to help fend off predators, their hooves are their best line of defence. Even wolves and bears are wary of a healthy adult moose.

Did you know? 3: Every winter, moose shed their antlers, but grow a beautiful new pair of velvety paddles to show off by the following October (mating season).

Collective noun possibilities: HERD, GANG, BUNCH, MOB, PARCEL

79. MOSQUITO

Description: Mosquitoes are small, flying insects with two wings, long, thin legs, antennae, and a very long proboscis – at least three times longer than their head.

Mosquito words: There are over 3,500 different mosquito species, including the YELLOW FEVER, ASIAN TIGER, SOUTHERN HOUSE, PITCHER PLANT and EASTERN SALTMARSH MOSQUITO. The ANOPHELES MOSQUITO is responsible for the transmission of malaria. MOSSIE, SKEETER and NIPPER are just a few of the nicknames that are sometimes used for mosquitoes. The word 'mosquito' is both Spanish and Portuguese for 'LITTLE FLY'.

Did you know? 1: Mosquitoes are officially the world's deadliest creatures, which is all down to the diseases they spread, including malaria, Zika virus and Dengue fever.

Did you know? 2: Only female mosquitoes bite.

Did you know? 3: Mosquitoes can drink up to three times their own weight in blood.

Collective noun possibilities: SCOURGE

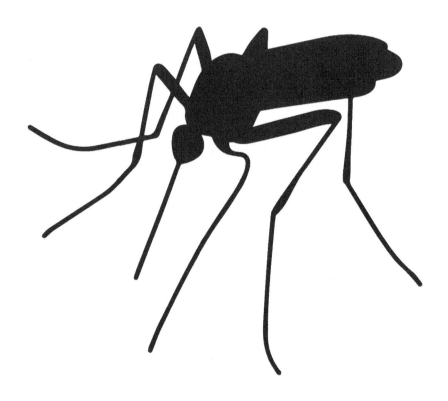

80. MOTH

Description: Moths are winged insects that are duller in colour than butterflies and have thicker bodies. Like butterflies, however, their wings are made up of scales. They tend to have either feathery or thick antennae with no club at the end. Some have very long tongues. Moths range from the size of a fingernail to the span of an average adult's hand.

Moth words: There are thousands of types of moth, including the COMMON CLOTHES, LUNA, PEPPERED, ATLAS, CARPET, DIAMONDBACK, JAPANESE SILK, ISABELLA TIGER and LITTLE BROWN APPLE MOTH.

Did you know? 1: Moths' hairy bodies make them great pollinators.

Did you know? 2: Some moths don't eat at all. The Luna moth, for example, only lives for about a week, during which time it just mates and lays eggs. It eats absolutely nothing as it doesn't even have a mouth.

Did you know? 3: Most nocturnally active moths are attracted to light.

Collective noun possibilities: ECLIPSE

81. MOUSE

Description: Mice are nocturnal rodents with a pointed nose, furry round body, prominent ears and thin tail.

Mouse words: There are hundreds of types of mice, including the HOUSE, FIELD, WOOD, SILKY POCKET, HARVEST, DEER, DORMOUSE, GOLDEN SPINY MOUSE and ZEBRA MOUSE. Male mice are BUCKS, females are DOES and babies are PINKIES or PUPS.

Did you know? 1: Theoretically, one mouse could have 150 offspring in a single year.

Did you know? 2: Mice can squeeze through a gap as thin as a pencil (roughly 6mm).

Did you know? 3: While communicating, mice make both ultrasonic as well as regular sounds.

Collective noun possibilities: MISCHIEF

82. NARWHAL

Description: Narwhals are medium-sized whales. Some male narwhals grow one long, clock-wise spiralled tusk, which is actually a tooth. Some grow two tusks and others don't grow any at all. Females occasionally grow a small tusk.

Narwhal words: A narwhal is one of two living species of the WHITE WHALE FAMILY, the other member being the beluga whale. Narwhals are sometimes thought of as the UNICORNS OF THE SEA.

Did you know? 1: A male narwhal's tusk can grow up to 10 feet long.

Did you know? 2: Narwhals change colour as they age. They start off blue-grey then turn blue-black, then mottled grey – and finally, as old narwhals, they are white.

Did you know? 3: According to Inuit myths, the narwhal was originally a woman with long hair that she twisted into a tusk. The woman's blind son tied her to a white whale, which then swam away with her. The woman drowned, but also changed into a narwhal.

Collective noun possibilities: BLESSING

83. OCTOPUS

Description: An octopus is a marine mollusc, famous for having eight sucker-covered limbs and a bulbous head. It is also a cephalopod, meaning that its head and feet are merged. Octopuses/octopodes (not octopi!) are boneless and have three hearts as well as blue blood.

Octopus words: These ocean-living creatures include the MOSAIC, ALGAE, STAR-SUCKER, GREATER BLUE-RINGED, MIMIC, SEVEN ARM, DUMBO, COCONUT, FLAPJACK, COMMON BLANKET and LILLIPUT LONG-ARM OCTOPUS. The GIANT PACIFIC OCTOPUS is the largest one of all.

Did you know? 1: Their limbs are called arms, legs or tentacles – officially 'muscular hydrostats' (structures of densely packed muscles, like a tongue or an elephant's trunk). Octopuses use their eight limbs to 'walk' on the sea floor. To swim, they push water through a muscular tube called a siphon.

Did you know? 2: They're great at camouflage and can change the colour of their body to mimic underwater objects like plants and rocks. The majority also squirt ink, which they use as camouflage.

Did you know? 3: They are very curious creatures and can become bored.

Collective noun possibilities: CONSORTIUM, APPLAUSE – although most are solitary creatures

84. ORANGUTAN

Description: An orangutan is an ape with distinctive, shaggy, orange-red fur. The arms of an orangutan are longer and more powerful than its legs. They are the largest of the arboreal mammals and spend most of their time in trees.

Orangutan words: There are three distinct species of orangutan: the BORNEAN, SUMATRAN and the TAPANULI ORANGUTAN. The name 'orangutan' means 'MAN OF THE FOREST' in Malay.

Did you know? 1: Some of their favourite foods are lychees, figs and mangosteens.

Did you know? 2: They have very flexible hip joints.

Did you know? 3: Their toes are big enough to grasp in the same way that a hand can.

Collective noun possibilities: CONGRESS

85. OSTRICH

Description: Ostriches are flightless birds. The Common Ostrich is the largest living bird species in the world and can reach up to 2.7m tall. Ostriches have a large, round, feathery body, a long, bare neck and long, muscular legs. Male Ostriches have black feathers and a white tail. Female plumage is mostly brown. Ostriches also have small heads, big eyes with long eyelashes, and a short beak.

Ostrich words: There are just two ostrich species: the COMMON OSTRICH and the SOMALI OSTRICH (aka the BLUE-NECKED OSTRICH).

Did you know? 1: Ostriches have three stomachs.

Did you know? 2: They are very fast runners and can run at approximately 50km/h for around half an hour.

Did you know? 3: Contrary to popular belief, ostriches do not stick their heads in the sand when being pursued by predators – they do it to check on their eggs – the largest eggs of any living bird. The word 'ostrich', however, remains a popular metaphor for someone unwilling to face up to their problems.

Collective noun possibilities: FLOCK, FLUTTER

86. OTTER

Description: Otters are semiaquatic mammals with long, agile bodies, relatively short limbs and a strong, muscular tail. They also have whiskers, powerful webbed feet, and most species have sharp claws.

Otter words: There are 13 otter species, including the GIANT, SMOOTH-COATED, AFRICAN CLAWLESS, MARINE, SPOTTED-NECK and HAIRY-NOSED OTTER. Males are BOARS, females are SOWS, and babies are PUPS, KITS or KITTENS.

Did you know? 1: All otter species love water and sometimes hold hands when sleeping in it. As well as looking very cute, this stops them from drifting away from each other.

Did you know? 2: River otters sometimes do a 'poop dance'. Apparently, their poop (aka spraint) generally smells quite pleasant – like Parma violets or freshly mown grass!

Did you know? 3: All ages of otters are very sociable and enjoy playing together. Playing keeps their family bonds strong and teaches the otter pups important skills. Their play often consists of water-sliding and 'juggling' stones.

Collective noun possibilities: BEVY, LODGE, ROMP

87. OWL

Description: Owls are birds with a large head, which can rotate approximately 135 degrees in both directions. They have forward-looking eye tubes rather than spherical eyeballs, meaning their eyes are fixed in one place – hence the need to turn their heads. They also have a sharply hooked beak, and feathers that are adapted to silent flight.

Owl words: There are over 225 owl species worldwide, including the ASHY-FACED, BARKING, BARN, CHOCOLATE BOOBOOK, BURROWING, CLOUD-FOREST PYGMY, ELF, FEARFUL, SHORT-EARED, SNOWY, SPECTACLED and BARE-LEGGED SCREECH OWL.

Did you know? 1: Owls often swallow their prey whole.

Did you know? 2: Not all owls are nocturnal; some are active daytime hunters.

Did you know? 3: Owls are popular birds for a number of reasons. As well as their many unique qualities, there are various legends and superstitions that surround them. They are also symbolic of wisdom and knowledge.

Collective noun possibilities: PARLIAMENT, STARE

88. PARROT

Description: Parrots are birds with sturdy, curved beaks, strong legs and clawed feet. Many of the different parrot species also have brightly coloured feathers. Parrots have zygodactyl toes – two toes facing forwards and two backwards, which helps provide them with the best possible grip.

Parrot words: Parrot species include COCKATIELS, LOVEBIRDS, PARAKEETS, LORIES, LORIKEETS, AFRICAN GREYS, AMAZONS, COCKATOOS, HAWK-HEADED PARROTS and MACAWS. Some of the most striking parrots are the RAINBOW LORIKEET, the CRIMSON ROSELLA and the SCARLET MACAW.

Did you know? 1: Parrots are believed to be one of the most intelligent species of birds. One particular African grey parrot, Alex, was thought to be as intelligent as an average 5-year-old child.

Did you know? 2: Some male and female parrots look identical to each other.

Did you know? 3: Some parrots can imitate human speech.

Collective noun possibilities: PANDEMONIUM, COMPANY

89. PEACOCK

Description: Peacocks are a large type of pheasant. The males are well-known for their stunning colours and impressive length and design of iridescent tail feathers. Females are smaller and their feathers (including their much shorter tails) are mainly grey or brown – although they do have iridescent necks. Both genders also have a crest on their head.

Peacock words: There are three species of PEAFOWL – the INDIAN (most familiar, with their stunning blue and green feathers), the GREEN (or JAVANESE) and the CONGO PEACOCK. Although only the male is officially known as a PEACOCK, PEAHENS (the females) and PEACHICKS are also often included when referring to 'peacocks'.

Did you know? 1: A peahen chooses her mate by the size of his tail feathers as well as by the number of eyespots he has on his train. Healthier, older males have tail feathers with more eyespots.

Did you know? 2: Peacocks shed their tail feathers each year after mating season.

Did you know? 3: In Greek mythology, peacocks symbolised immortality. Buddhists consider peafowl to represent wisdom, and peacocks are also one of the sacred birds within the Hindu culture.

Collective noun possibilities: OSTENTATION, PARTY, MUSTER, PRIDE

90. PEGASUS

Description: Pegasus was a beautiful, winged, mythical stallion from Greek mythology and is usually depicted as pure white. Although he never wore a saddle, he did sometimes wear an enchanted golden bridle.

The story of Pegasus: Pegasus was the offspring of Poseidon (Lord of the Sea) and Medusa (who had snakes for hair and was generally really nasty). When the Greek hero Perseus beheaded Medusa, Pegasus sprang from her neck. Pegasus is famous for helping the Greek gods and heroes. Eventually, Zeus took Pegasus to live with him on Mount Olympus. For his service and loyalty, Zeus transformed Pegasus into a constellation.

Did you know? 1: There was only ever one Pegasus. More than one would either be Pegasuses or Pegasi.

Did you know? 2: The powers of Pegasus include flight, carrying lightning bolts for Zeus and creating springs of water by thumping his foot on the ground.

Did you know? 3: Pegasus represents the ability of humans to imagine a world that is more magical than their own. He symbolises freedom, limitless imagination and creativity.

Collective noun possibilities: SOAR, WINGING, SWOOP – albeit that he was a one-off

91. PELICAN

Description: Pelicans are large water birds with a long, pouched beak, short legs and webbed feet.

Pelican words: There are eight species of pelican. These are the AMERICAN WHITE, BROWN, PERUVIAN, GREAT WHITE, AUSTRALIAN, PINK-BACKED, DALMATIAN and SPOT-BILLED PELICAN.

Did you know? 1: They use their pouch to catch fish in, then drain off the water and immediately swallow the fish. They don't use their pouch to store fish.

Did you know? 2: Although they are heavy, pelicans have air-sacs in their bones, which helps them to keep buoyant in water.

Did you know? 3: It used to be believed that the pelican would pierce its own chest with its beak to allow its hungry chicks to feed off its blood. This caused the pelican to become a symbol of Christianity, representing Christ's sacrifice for humanity.

Collective noun possibilities: SQUADRON, POD, POUCH, SCOOP

92. PENGUIN

Description: Penguins are aquatic, flightless birds with flippers rather than wings. Adult penguins are different combinations of black, white, yellow, orange and blue, depending on the species.

Penguin words: Penguins are only found in the Southern Hemisphere and include EMPEROR, GENTOO, KING, LITTLE, ROCKHOPPER, CHINSTRAP, YELLOW-EYED and MACARONI PENGUINS.

Did you know? 1: Their black and white colouring is called countershading – dark on the back and light on the front, providing them with camouflage from both above and below when swimming.

Did you know? 2: Penguins can drink seawater and have a gland that removes the salt from their bloodstream. The penguin then sneezes out the excess sodium.

Did you know? 3: Penguins are able to recognise each other because of each individual's unique call.

Collective noun possibilities: RAFT, WADDLE, CRÈCHE, COLONY, HUDDLE, TUXEDO

93. PHOENIX

Description: The phoenix is a supernatural bird and stories about it are rooted in Greek mythology. Descriptions vary, although it is often portrayed as resembling an eagle, but with red and gold plumage and long tail feathers.

Phoenix words: A phoenix is said to live for 500 years, at which point it builds a nest made from incense and sacred materials and burns itself up, turning into ash. From these ashes, a new, young phoenix will arise. There is only ever one phoenix alive at any one time. The phoenix is also known as the FLAME BIRD. FENGHUANG, a bird from Chinese mythology, has superficial similarities to the phoenix and is sometimes referred to as the CHINESE PHOENIX.

Did you know? 1: The tears of a phoenix are said to possess amazing healing powers.

Did you know? 2: A phoenix's weakness is iron; when a phoenix touches iron, it will burn.

Did you know? 3: The phoenix symbolises immortality, resurrection and life after death.

Collective noun possibilities: ODYSSEY – although only one ever exists at any one time

94. PIG

Description: Pigs are even-toed ungulates with stout bodies and short legs. They usually have thick skin with some bristles. A pig's snout has a large round disc of cartilage at the end, making it ideal for rooting around. Many breeds of pig have curly tails.

Pig words: Some pigs are wild, others are domesticated. Pig breeds are common throughout the world and include the WILD BOAR, PYGMY HOG, JAVAN WARTY PIG, BORNEAN BEARDED PIG, GIANT FOREST HOG, BUSH-PIG, TAMWORTH, BRITISH SADDLEBACK, IRON AGE PIG, LINCOLNSHIRE CURLY COAT, VIETNAMESE POT-BELLIED PIG and various WARTHOGS. The largest pig ever recorded was a SWINE called BIG BILL, who was 5 feet tall. Male pigs are BOARS, females are SOWS, and young pigs are PIGLETS.

Did you know? 1: Pigs are sociable animals who enjoy forming close bonds. They use over 20 distinct grunts and squeals to communicate, and mother pigs 'sing' to their babies while nursing.

Did you know? 2: They don't have sweat glands, which is why they like to spend time wallowing in mud.

Did you know? 3: Pigs can remember objects, perceive time, navigate over long distances and be playful – all signs of intelligence.

Collective noun possibilities: LITTER, DRIFT, DROVE, TEAM, SOUNDER

95. PLATYPUS

Description: Platypuses are classified as monotremes – predatory mammals that lay eggs. They have a flat, brown, furry body, a broad, flat tail, short legs and a beak.

Platypus words: There is only one type of platypus, which is also sometimes referred to as the DUCK-BILLED PLATYPUS. Names that are in fairly common use for a baby platypus are a PUGGLE or a PLATYPUP.

Did you know? 1: When they were discovered in 1798, British scientists thought that they were a hybrid hoax made up of an otter or a beaver, and a duck.

Did you know? 2: Platypuses have a spur on each hind leg, which is connected to a venomous gland.

Did you know? 3: They use electronic impulses to detect objects in the dark.

Collective noun possibilities: PADDLE – although they don't tend to gather in groups

96. POLAR BEAR

Description: Polar bears are classed as marine mammals as they spend the majority of their time in or on the ocean. They are huge, hyper-carnivorous bears with large paws that are great for swimming.

Polar bear words: There are 19 URSUS MARITIMUS (polar bear) species. Throughout the Arctic, polar bears are called by a variety of different names, including NANOOK, ICE BEAR, SEA BEAR and WHITE BEAR. Grizzly-Polar bear hybrids already exist. They are known as GROLAR BEARS (when the male is a grizzly) and PIZZLY BEARS (when the male is a polar bear).

Did you know? 1: They hold their back legs behind them like a rudder when swimming.

Did you know? 2: Polar bears are the largest land carnivores in the world and can weigh as much as ten average men.

Did you know? 3: Polar bears are actually black. Their skin is black and their hairs are hollow, giving the impression that they are white.

Collective noun possibilities: CELEBRATION – although they're generally solitary

97. PORCUPINE

Description: Porcupines are large rodents with part of their coat made up of sharp quills, which in some cases can reach up to 50cm long.

Porcupine words: There are OLD WORLD PORCUPINES and NEW WORLD PORCUPINES. They include BRUSH-TAILED, CRESTED, HAIRY, LONG-TAILED and STUMP-TAILED PORCUPINES. Baby porcupines are called PORCUPETTES.

Did you know? 1: The quills generally lie flat until the porcupine feels threatened, at which point, they help to protect the porcupine by jumping quickly to attention. The quills don't shoot out but do often get caught up in the bodies of any predators who are brave enough to attempt an attack. Some quills – those with bars or scales – tend to be more hazardous than others.

Did you know? 2: Porcupines spend quite a lot of their time sitting quietly in trees.

Did you know? 3: When looking for food on the ground, they use their good sense of smell to locate it and their short legs to wander off in the right direction to find it.

Collective noun possibilities: PRICKLE

98. PRAWN

Description: A prawn is a small aquatic crustacean with a long, thin body, a semi-transparent exoskeleton, ten legs and very long antennae. Prawns also have large eyes and a fan-shaped tail called a telson.

Prawn words: Prawn species vary in length from really tiny to around 16cm. They include PINK, TIGER, WHITE, GIANT RIVER, GLASS and BANANA PRAWNS.

Did you know? 1: Chameleon prawns can gradually change colour according to their surroundings.

Did you know? 2: Prawns have blue blood.

Did you know? 3: They can swim, crawl and dart.

Collective noun possibilities: CLUTCH

99. PRAYING MANTIS

Description: A praying mantis is a typically green or brown insect with a triangular head, two bulging, compound eyes and three simple eyes. Its two front legs are bent as if in prayer. Some have body shapes that make them look like a leaf or a branch.

Praying mantis words: There are hundreds of praying mantis species throughout the world, including the DEAD LEAF, ORCHID, CHINESE, GHOST, WANDERING VIOLIN, ARIZONA and UNICORN MANTIS. The word 'mantis' comes from the Greek word 'MANTIKOS' and means 'PROPHET'.

Did you know? 1: The praying mantis's angelic pose allows it to quickly extend its arms to capture its prey.

Did you know? 2: It's well-known that the female praying mantis often eats her partner during or after mating. Some males attack the female and injure her in an attempt to stop themselves from being eaten.

Did you know? 3: The praying mantis is the only known creature to have only one ear – making it an 'auditory cyclops'. Its ear is on the underside of its belly.

Collective noun possibilities: CONGREGATION, TEMPLE, DIVINITY

100. PTERODACTYL

Description: 'Pterodactyl' represents a number of winged reptiles that lived during the Late Jurassic and Cretaceous periods. Each had a very long fourth finger on either side, to which its wings were attached, a crest on its head, and a long bird-like beak. They existed in a variety of sizes.

Pterodactyl words: The word 'PTERODACTYLUS' comes from Greek and means 'WING FINGER'.

Did you know? 1: Pterodactyls were capable of 'flapping flight' rather than simply gliding.

Did you know? 2: Their wings were made from a skin and muscle membrane, similar to webbed feet in ducks.

Did you know? 3: Pterodactylus was a carnivore and probably ate fish and small animals.

Collective noun possibilities: SKIM, SWOOP, FLEET

101. PUFFERFISH

Description: Pufferfish are so-called for their ability to inflate themselves - often to more than double their original size by swallowing water when they feel threatened. They are scaleless with rough or spiky skin and range from one inch to two feet in length. They also have teeth that are fused together to create a sort of beak.

Pufferfish words: Pufferfish are also known as BLOWFISH and include the WHITE-SPOTTED, SHARP-NOSE, MAP, STARRY and BLUNT-HEAD PUFFER.

Did you know? 1: Most pufferfish are highly toxic and are amongst the most poisonous creatures on earth. They don't bite or sting, but their bodies contain a toxin (tetraodotoxin) that's deadly to humans, far stronger than cyanide – and with no antidote! The toxin is secreted across their bodies, which means that even licking or touching a pufferfish is very dangerous.

Did you know? 2: A pufferfish dish, known as fugu, is considered to be a Japanese delicacy – despite the toxin in one fish being enough to kill 30 people. Appealing as the taste and look of fugu may be, its poison continues to claim a number of people each year.

Did you know? 3: With some pufferfish, the spines aren't visible until the fish puffs up.

Collective noun possibilities: WUNCH, POKE, TOXOID

102. RABBIT

Description: Rabbits are crepuscular (mainly active at dawn and dusk), small, furry mammals with long ears, a fluffy tail and strong back legs. They have four webbed toes on their hind feet and five toes on their front paws. Their teeth grow throughout their lives and are great for gnawing.

Rabbit words: There are over 300 breeds of domestic rabbits, which include the AMERICAN FUZZY LOP, ANGORA, BOURBONNAIS GREY, BROWN CHESTNUT OF LORRAINE, CHEQUERED GIANT, CHINCHILLA, HARLEQUIN and LIONHEAD RABBIT. Some wild rabbit breeds include COTTONTAILS as well as the PYGMY, EUROPEAN, SUMATRAN STRIPED and VOLCANO RABBIT. Rabbits are also known as BUNNIES or BUNNY RABBITS.

Did you know? 1: Carrots may be considered typical rabbit food but in fact carrots are high in sugar and only really suitable to be eaten by rabbits occasionally. Hay and grass should be the main diet for rabbits.

Did you know? 2: Despite symbolising harmlessness and timidity, rabbits are banned from being taken on certain ferries. They are said to have chewed their way through the hull of a ship in the 17th century, causing the drowning of lots of sailors.

Did you know? 3: When they're happy, rabbits sometimes binky. This is a cheerful little hop in the air that they do where they slightly twist their body and kick out their feet.

Collective noun possibilities: BURY, KINDLE, WARREN, COLONY, DOWN, NEST, TRIP, FLUFFLE

103. RAT

Description: Rats are rodents with a slim, pointed head, lightly furred ears and obvious whiskers. They also have furry bodies, fairly long legs and long, sharp claws. A rat's tail is thicker than a mouse's tail and has a scaly texture with tiny hairs.

Rat words: Rats are very widespread and include the ROOF, BROWN, GIANT, KANGAROO and BULLDOG RAT.

Did you know? 1: They don't sweat or pant to release heat. Instead, they control their body temperature by expanding or contracting blood vessels in their tails.

Did you know? 2: Rats have a useful set of skills that help them to survive. They are great swimmers, some species being able to swim for over a mile at any one time. They can also hold their breath for up to three minutes and are able to chew through wood, plastic, soft concrete and many other materials.

Did you know? 3: Rats are both loathed and loved. Rats and their fleas became infamous for carrying and spreading certain diseases, such as typhus, the bubonic plague (aka the Black Death), and around 40 other diseases. However, more recently, scientists have found parasites on humans to be a more likely match for the spread of the Black Death in 14th and 19th century Europe. In some places, (the Karni Mata Temple in India, for example) rats are worshipped. They have also become popular pets as they are easy to look after, don't have a strong smell and rarely bite.

Collective noun possibilities: MISCHIEF, PACK, PLAGUE, COLONY, SWARM

104. RHINICEROS

Description: Considered the second-largest land animal (to elephants), the rhino has a sturdy body with a large head, relatively short legs and a short tail. A striking feature is the large horn or horns (some species have two) that rhinos have in the middle of their faces.

Rhino words: There are currently five species of rhino alive today – the BLACK RHINO, WHITE RHINO (both found in Africa), as well as the INDIAN, JAVAN and SUMATRAN RHINOS (found in southern Asia). Male rhinos are BULLS, females are COWS and juveniles are CALVES.

Did you know? 1: A rhino's horn grows continuously throughout its life.

Did you know? 2: Rhinos love rolling in mud, which gives them a protective layer, keeps them cool, and helps to prevent them being bitten by insects.

Did you know? 3: Although fairly quiet animals, rhinos do make lots of different noises. They snort, make sneeze-like sounds, scream, grunt, growl, moo, pant, squeal and even trumpet.

Collective noun possibilities: CRASH

105. SALAMANDER

Description: Salamanders are a type of amphibian that look like a cross between a frog and a lizard. They have slim bodies, short legs, and long tails. Some have gills and take in oxygen through their skin; others breathe through their lungs. Some have four legs, others have just two.

Salamander words: There are over 700 species of salamander, including the FIRE, MARBLED, JEFFERSON, OLYMPIC TORRENT, LONG-TOED, FOUR-TOED, CLOUDED and NORTHERN SLIMY SALAMANDER. Most species are small. The CHINESE GIANT SALAMANDER is the world's largest amphibian and can grow to up to 1.8m long

Did you know? 1: The skin of a salamander is poisonous, requiring humans to wash their hands thoroughly after touching them.

Did you know? 2: Salamanders can regenerate lost limbs, and even parts of their lungs and brain, within a few weeks of damaging or losing them.

Did you know? 3: Salamanders will sometimes eat other salamanders that are smaller than themselves.

Collective noun possibilities: HERD, BAND, CONGRESS

106. SCORPION

Description: A scorpion is a predatory arachnid, and like all arachnids, has eight legs. Scorpions also have a pair of large, grasping pincers and a segmented tail with a venomous sting at the end.

Scorpion words: There are around 2,000 scorpion species, including the ARIZONA BARK SCORPION, DEATH STALKER, HOTTENTOTTA and GIANT HAIRY SCORPION.

Did you know? 1: Scorpions perform a 'dance' before they mate. This ritual involves the couple holding pincers while moving around.

Did you know? 2: Adult scorpions have fluorescent chemicals in their exoskeleton, which means they glow in UV light.

Did you know? 3: They use their pincers to quickly grab their prey, then administer poison using their sting to either kill or stun their victim. Although the venom from scorpions contains deadly toxins, helpful chemicals have also been discovered within some venom compounds.

Collective noun possibilities: BED, NEST

107. SEAHORSE

Description: Seahorses are upright fish with heads that resemble land-based horses. They also have a brood pouch, similar to that of a kangaroo. Their body is covered in tiny spines, and they have a strong, curly tail. They don't have a stomach or teeth.

Seahorse words: There are currently 47 known species of these small marine fish, including the SHORT-SNOUTED, BIG-BELLY, TIGER TAIL, LEAFY SEA-DRAGON, GIRAFFE, CROWNED and JAPANESE PYGMY SEAHORSE. Seahorses belong to the hippocampus genus, meaning 'HORSE SEA MONSTER'.

Did you know? 1: Seahorses have some amazing abilities. It's the father who gives birth. Feeding involves sucking in their food and swallowing it whole. And they can change colour to camouflage or express themselves.

Did you know? 2: Each seahorse has a unique identifier – a small crown called a coronet.

Did you know? 3: They use their tails as a weapon to battle over food or territory and to attach themselves to vegetation. Mated pairs sometimes link tails, rather like humans might hold hands.

Collective noun possibilities: SHOAL, HERD

108. SEA URCHIN

Description: Sea urchins are small sea animals with hard, spherical shells that are covered in spines. Although they live on the ocean floor and cannot swim, they do have tiny tube-shaped feet, which they use to help them move. They come in lots of different colours.

Sea urchin words: There are around 950 species of sea urchin – also known as SEA HEDGEHOGS. Some flatter, burrowing sea urchins are known as SAND DOLLARS, SAND CAKES, CAKE URCHINS and SEA BISCUITS.

Did you know? 1: Some sea urchins have venom in their feet, others have it in their spines. Most sea urchins are harmless, but some, like the long-spined sea urchin found in south Florida, is definitely best avoided.

Did you know? 2: The bodies of mature sea urchins are made up of 5 symmetrical sections.

Did you know? 3: Sea urchins can live for up to 200 years!

Collective noun possibilities: WAKE, HERD, RASH, SWELL, RIPPLE, SPIKE, SKEWER

109. SEAL

Description: Seals are semiaquatic, mostly marine mammals that are found along coastal areas. They have a body-shape which is round in the middle and tapers towards the tail. They also have four flippers (each with five webbed digits covered in hair), a layer of blubber under their skin to keep them warm, whiskers and a slick fur coat.

Seal words: TRUE SEALS include HARBOUR, RIBBON, GALAPAGOS FUR, GREY, NORTHERN ELEPHANT and BEARDED SEALS. The HARP SEAL pup may be the cutest of them all.

Did you know? 1: Seals are excellent swimmers and the whiskers on their rounded faces are highly sensitive, allowing them to hunt for food, even when visibility is poor.

Did you know? 2: They can sleep underwater and some can hold their breath for up to 2 hours.

Did you know? 3: A seal in a classic 'banana pose' suggests that it is happy and content and/or that it may be regulating its body temperature while keeping its extremities dry.

Collective noun possibilities: COLONY, TEAM, HERD, POD, BOB

110. SHARK

Description: Sharks are medium to large fish with a prominent dorsal fin and – depending on the species – a combination of pectoral, second dorsal, pelvic and caudal fins. Most are predatory and many have sharp, serrated or triangular-shaped teeth. Most sharks have between 5 and 7 gill slits on each side of their head.

Shark words: There are more than 500 species of shark, including the GREAT WHITE, TIGER, BULL, BASKING, GREAT HAMMERHEAD, NURSE, BLUNT-NOSE, SPINY DOGFISH, MEGAMOUTH, SPOTTED WOBBEGONG and COOKIE CUTTER SHARK.

Did you know? 1: Sharks don't have bones. Instead, their skeletons are made from cartilage, like the tips of our noses. This helps them to be lighter and therefore more buoyant.

Did you know? 2: They have small black spots around their face area. These are electroreceptor organs that allow them to sense electromagnetic fields as well as temperature shifts in the ocean.

Did you know? 3: Shark skin feels like sandpaper. This is due to their scales, known as dermal denticles, which help to reduce friction when they swim.

Collective noun possibilities: HERD, FRENZY, SCHOOL, SHIVER

111. SHEEP

Description: Sheep are sturdy, even-toed ungulates, meaning they have two primary 'toes' per foot rather than a single hoof. Some breeds have horns that grow from the tops of their heads. All sheep grow a woolly coat.

Sheep words: Sheep breeds include the CHEVIOT, DORSET, HAMPSHIRE, OXFORD, SUFFOLK, TUNIS, AMERICAN BLACKBELLY, CALIFORNIA RED, MOUFLON, ICELANDIC and JACOB SHEEP. Female sheep are called EWES, males are RAMS and young sheep are LAMBS.

Did you know? 1: The wool of a sheep will continue to grow all its life.

Did you know? 2: Sheep have rectangular pupils. This gives them a wide field of vision without' having to turn their heads, and helps them to avoid predators.

Did you know? 3: Sheep are capable of having an array of feelings. Studies have shown that they can feel happy, sad, angry and bored. They have even been shown to be either optimistic or pessimistic!

Collective noun possibilities: FLOCK, HERD, DROVE

112. SHETLAND PONY

Description: A Shetland pony is a particular breed of Scottish pony, originating from the Shetland islands to the north of mainland Scotland. Shetland ponies are strong for their size and are used as pack ponies as well as for riding and driving. They have a heavy coat, a broad back with a deep girth, short legs and dainty feet.

Pony words: Other pony breeds include the DARTMOOR, EXMOOR, NEW FOREST, CONNEMARA, ERISKAY, HIGHLAND and WELSH PONY. Shetland ponies are sometimes called SHELTIES.

Did you know? 1: Shelties are great for beginners who are keen to keep a pony as they don't need too much food or water and are strong, brave and hardy.

Did you know? 2: Shetland ponies have a double coat – an outer coat that they shed in the spring and summer and an inner coat that they keep all year round.

Did you know? 3: Although any equine under 14.2 hands is considered to be a pony, a Shetland pony shouldn't be any taller than 11.5 hands in the USA / 11 hands in the UK.

Collective noun possibilities: STRING, HERD, MARMALADE

113. SKUNK

Description: Skunks are furry, nocturnal mammals with a bushy tail. Most species are around the size of a house cat. They come in a variety of colours and patterns and are largely black and white. The common striped skunk is typically black with a white V down its back and a white bar between its eyes.

Skunk words: Skunks and stink badgers belong to the same family and are divided into four genera (types): SKUNKS, HOG-NOSED SKUNKS, SPOTTED SKUNKS and STINK BADGERS.

Did you know? 1: Skunks are well-known for being able to spray an unpleasant, pungent-smelling liquid called musk.

Did you know? 2: When skunks feel threatened, they stamp their front feet and raise their tail.

Did you know? 3: They sometimes do a dance before spraying.

Collective noun possibilities: SURFEIT, STENCH

114. SLUG

Description: A slug is a gastropod mollusc without a shell – or at least without much of one. Some slugs have hidden shells and there are also semi-slugs, which have tiny shells that are far too small for them to hide in. A slug is slimy, soft-bodied and tough-skinned, and is like a cousin to the snail. Slugs have four retractable tentacles (used for sensing their environment), blowholes (for breathing through) and thousands of tiny protrusions that act like teeth.

Slug words: Slug species include the BLACK, YELLOW, WHITE-SOLED, LARGE SPOTTED GARDEN and GREY FIELD SLUG. The BANANA SLUG looks very much like its namesake.

Did you know? 1: Slugs are cold, sticky creatures that tend to come out mostly at night, leaving a trail of slime wherever they go. Their slime or mucus is a substance between a liquid and a solid called liquid crystal.

Did you know? 2: Slugs move by using the one giant muscle that makes up their body.

Did you know? 3: Slugs aren't toxic to humans but can be to certain animals.

Collective noun possibilities: CORNUCOPIA, PHLEGM, SLIME

115. SNAIL

Description: A snail is a gastropod, meaning 'stomach foot'. It is a soft-bodied slug-like creature, typically with a spiral-shaped shell consisting of coils and whorls. Several species of land snails have hairy shells. Snails have four antennae (aka tentacles). The longer two are used for smelling and seeing, the shorter two for smelling and tasting.

Snail words: There are thousands of LAND, SEA and FRESHWATER SNAILS throughout the world. These include the MILK, GIANT AFRICAN LAND, MOON, VAMPIRE, PERIWINKLE and LAVA SNAIL. The GIANT WHELK has a shell that can be up to 70cm long. Snail shells come in a variety of sizes as well as spiral-based shapes, including GLOBULAR, DISCOIDAL, CONICAL, ELONGATED-TURRETED and FLAT-COILED.

Did you know? 1: Snails are one of the slowest-moving creatures in the world.

Did you know? 2: They can typically withdraw their head and foot from their shell, but they can't abandon their shells entirely because they are physically attached to them.

Did you know? 3: Conches are very large sea snails, which when empty, have been used as musical instruments (shell trumpets) for thousands of years.

Collective noun possibilities: ROUT, WALK, HOOD, ESCARGATOIRE

116. SNAKE

Description: Snakes are reptiles with a long, slender body, no limbs, and no external ears or eyelids. Their skin is covered in scales. Many snakes have a forked tongue – which allows them to sense the direction that a smell is coming from.

Snake words: Around 3,000 snake species are known to exist, including the GRASS SNAKE, BOA CONSTRICTOR, EYELASH VIPER, CARPET PYTHON, YELLOW-LIPPED SEA KRAIT, BOOMSLANG, RUBBER BOA, WESTERN DIAMONDBACK RATTLESNAKE, COTTONMOUTH, KING COBRA and BLACK MAMBA. The RETICULATED PYTHON is the world's longest snake and can grow up to 6 metres long. The most venomous snake in the world is the INLAND TAIPAN. Different snakes make different noises, including HISSING, RATTLING, BUZZING, SHRIEKING and GROWLING.

Did you know? 1: Venomous snakes make venom in their salivary glands, which is then pushed out through their fangs when they bite into their prey. Having killed their victim, they then use their flexible jaws to open their mouth extremely wide to eat – sometimes even eating prey that's bigger than they are.

Did you know? 2: Constrictor snakes either swallow their victims alive or squeeze them to death first.

Did you know? 3: Snakes shed their skin between 4 and 12 times a year. as they always continue to grow, and the outer layer of skin becomes too tight.

Collective noun possibilities: BED, DEN, PIT, NEST, RHUMBA

117. SQUID

Description: Squid are invertebrates that are related to octopuses and cuttlefish. They have a tube-shaped body, eight arms with suckers, a small, rod-shaped internal shell called a pen and two tentacles. They also have a beak and an outer bag-like covering called a mantle, which protects the squid's internal organs – including their three hearts. Squid also have an ink sac and will use the ink they produce as a defence mechanism.

Squid words: Squid species include the PYGMY SQUID (which is about the size of a small fingernail), and the COLOSSAL SQUID (which can grow up to 12 metres long).

Did you know? 1: Squid shoot out their tentacles to catch prey. They then use their arms to pass the prey into their mouth.

Did you know? 2: Deep-water squid have organs that glow in the dark.

Did you know? 3: Relative to size, squid have the largest eyes of any living creature. The eyes of giant squid are as big as footballs. This helps them to see well in the depths of the ocean. They also have in-built contact lenses to help protect their eyes and to stay focused on their prey.

Collective noun possibilities: SQUAD, SHOAL, SCHOOL

118. SQUIRREL

Description: Squirrels are smallish rodents with slender bodies, large eyes, and distinctive bushy tails. The colour of their fur varies depending on the species. Flying squirrels glide rather than fly. They have flaps of skin, which connect their limbs and allow them to coast through the air.

Squirrel words: The squirrel family includes TREE SQUIRRELS, GROUND SQUIRRELS (including CHIPMUNKS and PRAIRIE DOGS) and FLYING SQUIRRELS.

Did you know? 1: The four front teeth of squirrels never stop growing. This means they can gnaw on as many nuts, seeds, bark, fruit, etc. as they want to without their teeth wearing down.

Did you know? 2: Squirrels make various noises in order to communicate, but their main way to do so is by using their tail.

Did you know? 3: Symbolic of playfulness, energy, and being prepared, squirrels are known for hoarding their food, either by scatter-hoarding (stashing their food in a variety of places), or larder-hoarding (keeping it all in one spot). Scatter-hoarding squirrels are essential to the spread of oak trees.

Collective noun possibilities: DRAY, SCURRY

119. STARFISH

Description: Starfish aren't actually fish, they're invertebrates. Most have spiky skin and usually five arms – although some have many more. They have tiny tube-like feet on their arms, which help them to move. Their 'eyes' (on the ends of their arms) allow them to distinguish between light and dark.

Starfish words: There are hundreds of different types of starfish (aka SEA STARS), including the NECKLACE STARFISH, CHORIASTER STARFISH (aka the DOUGHBOY or GRANULATED SEA STAR), CROWN OF THORNS STARFISH, CHOCOLATE CHIP SEA STAR and the SUNFLOWER SEA STAR (the largest starfish species known, with an arm-span of over a metre).

Did you know? 1: Starfish are more solitary than social. However, they do sometimes gather in large groups to feed.

Did you know? 2: They protect themselves with their hard, knobbly outer layer and some also come in striking colours, which helps them to camouflage themselves amongst certain types of coral.

Did you know? 3: Some starfish have the ability to regrow their lost or damaged limbs.

Collective noun possibilities: GALAXY, CONSTELLATION

Description: The stegosaurus was a large, herbivorous, four-legged dinosaur from the Late Jurassic period. It had a small head relative to its body, a turtle-like beak, and kite-shaped upright plates along either side of its spine and tail. The stegosaurus grew up to nine metres long and up to four metres tall.

Stegosaurus words: The name stegosaurus means ROOFED LIZARD. There are three recognised species of stegosaurus: the HOOFED ROOF LIZARD, the NARROW-FACED ROOF LIZARD and the FURROWED ROOF LIZARD.

Did you know? 1: The brain of the stegosaurus was about the size of a ping-pong ball.

Did you know? 2: It was a slow-moving dinosaur, possibly able to walk at up to 4 miles per hour.

Did you know? 3: The stegosaurus was similar in weight to today's African elephant – around 5 tonnes.

Collective noun possibilities: CRASH

121. SWAN

Description: Swans are members of the same family as ducks and geese. They are large water birds with elongated, curved necks who mate for life and are known for their majestic, graceful appearance. There are black as well as white swans.

Swan words: Swan species include the MUTE, TRUMPETER, WHOOPER, BLACK-NECKED and TUNDRA SWAN. A male swan is called a COB, a female is a PEN and baby swans are CYGNETS.

Did you know? 1: Although swans are generally peaceful, they do sometimes display moments of aggression (including making hissing noises), especially when protecting their eggs or young.

Did you know? 2: Cygnus – the Latin word for swan – is a constellation also known as the northern cross. The constellation represents Orpheus, from Greek mythology, who was transformed into a swan when he died.

Did you know? 3: Swans represent elegance and refinement.

Collective noun possibilities: WEDGE, BANK, HERD, BEVY, FLOCK

122. SWORDFISH

Description: Swordfish are long, predatory fish – sometimes up to 14 feet long – with a round body and a long, pointed bill. They also have a large crescent-shaped tail (the caudal fin) as well as dorsal and pectoral fins. By the time they are adults, swordfish no longer have any teeth or scales.

Swordfish words: Swordfish are also sometimes known as BROADBILLS. Their Latin name is XIPHIAS GLADIUS, 'GLADIUS' meaning 'SWORD'.

Did you know? 1: They have special organs beside their eyes that keep their eyes and brain warmer in cold water, which in turn helps them to see better.

Did you know? 2: They use their 'sword' to stun their prey by moving their head quickly from side to side. This slashing movement can knock their prey unconscious, making it easier to catch.

Did you know? 3: They are one of the fastest fish in the ocean, sometimes swimming at more than 50 miles per hour.

Collective noun possibilities: ARMOURY, DUEL (two)

123. TADPOLE

Description: Tadpoles are the tailed aquatic larva of frogs and toads between the stages of egg and adulthood in their life-cycle. Tadpoles have short, oval bodies, small mouths, and long, broad tails. They are often part see-through and use internal gills to breathe. There is a huge variation in the sizes of tadpoles, depending on the species. The tadpoles of the Paradoxical frog, for example, can grow to a massive 11 inches.

Tadpole words: Tadpoles are also sometimes known as POLLYWOGS – a word that comes from the Middle English 'POLWYGLE', meaning 'HEAD WIGGLE', which describes how they move.

Did you know? 1: Once the tadpole has grown big enough, it emerges from its jelly-covered egg. Some tadpoles don't move for a few days after hatching. Once released from their eggs, they take 14 -16 weeks to develop into miniature froglets or toadlets.

Did you know? 2: Tadpoles inhabit rivers, streams, ponds, marshes and lakes – even puddles. Some tadpoles are terrestrial and live in damp places near to a water source.

Did you know? 3: It's thought that they may play an important role in helping to conserve the ecosystems of freshwater streams etc.

Collective noun possibilities: SHOAL, SCHOOL

124. TARANTULA

Description: Tarantulas are typically large, hairy spiders. They have eight legs as well as eight tiny eyes. Some have leg spans of up to 11 inches. Their colours and size vary.

Tarantula words: Tarantula species include the ANTILLES PINK TOE, BRAZILIAN BLACK, BRAZILIAN PINK BIRD-EATING, CHACO GOLDEN-KNEE, COSTA RICAN ZEBRA, DESERT BLONDE, GREENBOTTLE BLUE and HONDURAN CURLY HAIR TARANTULA. The largest tarantula in the world is the GOLIATH BIRD-EATING TARANTULA.

Did you know? 1: The tarantula doesn't spin a web to trap its next meal. Instead, it bites its prey with its long, curved fangs, and in doing so, injects its victim with venom. It then secretes digestive enzymes, which turn the body of the victim into a soft pulp, then drinks its prey through its straw-like mouth. Fortunately, there are only a few species of tarantula which have a bite that is dangerous to humans – in most cases, their bite is no more harmful than a bee sting.

Did you know? 2: Although tarantulas don't spin webs to catch their prey, they do create doors, walls and tunnels out of silk in order to build better homes for themselves.

Did you know? 3: The name tarantula originates from a town called Taranto in Italy. Legend has it that there was a small species of spider living there that had a fatal bite. The only way to avoid succumbing to its venom was to sweat out the poison by dancing. This is where the name for the frenzied folk dance, the tarantella, comes from.

Collective noun possibilities: COLONY, STING, WOUND

125. THREE-HEADED DOG

Description: A three-headed dog is a magical, ferocious creature that is larger and stronger than any non-magical dog. One head represents the past, one the present, and the third head is the future.

Three-headed dog words: In Greek mythology, there was a three-headed dog known as CERBERUS, which guarded the underworld. Another name for Cerberus was the HOUND OF HADES or HELL HOUND. In Harry Potter, there's a three-headed guard dog called FLUFFY.

Did you know? 1: Cerberus was the offspring of Echidna (a hybrid half-woman, half-serpent) and Typhon (a gigantic monster).

Did you know? 2: The powers of Cerberus were: great strength (to prevent any souls from leaving the underworld once he'd let them in), the ability to see in a number of directions at once, and being able to attack various opponents simultaneously. Cerberus was also said to be able to breathe fire.

Did you know? 3: His weakness was the inability to stop himself from falling asleep to the sound of music.

Collective noun possibilities: LULLABY, SNARL, TIMESPAN

126. TIGER

Description: The tiger is the largest big cat (with the Siberian tiger reaching up to 3.3 metres/10 feet long). One of the most striking aspects of a tiger is its orange and white fur with dark stripes.

Tiger words: The BENGAL tiger is the most common subspecies. Some other living subspecies are the SIBERIAN, INDO-CHINESE, MALAYAN, SOUTH CHINA and SUMATRAN TIGER.

Did you know? 1: The bite force of a tiger is almost twice that of a lion.

Did you know? 2: Their flexible spines and long back legs allow them to jump up to ten metres high.

Did you know? 3: Unlike most other cats, tigers are great swimmers and enjoy being in water.

Collective noun possibilities: STREAK, AMBUSH

127. TOAD

Description: Toads are amphibians that are similar to frogs but tend to look less athletic, more squat, and with shorter limbs. Their skin is rougher, drier and more warty-looking than frogs' skin. Toads also don't have teeth – unlike some of their frog relatives, and toad spawn is laid in long strings – unlike frog spawn, which is laid in clumps.

Toad words: Toad species include the COMMON MIDWIFE, GOLDEN, ORIENTAL FIRE-BELLIED, OAK, EASTERN SPADEFOOT, NATTERJACK and RED-SPOTTED TOAD. The COMMON TOAD – or BUFO BUFO – is the UK's most prevalent toad. Young toads are called TOADLETS.

Did you know? 1: Toads have glands (the warty-looking parts on their back), which secrete a thick, milky-looking poison to help them defend themselves. Some species also have glands on their limbs.

Did you know? 2: A toad's tongue is attached to the front of its mouth, which makes it easier for it to catch bugs.

Did you know? 3: Toads like to hide in damp, dark places.

Collective noun possibilities: KNOT, NEST, LUMP, SQUIGGLE

128. TORTOISE

Description: Tortoises are slow-moving (0.2 mph), land-dwelling reptiles. They are usually green or brown, have dome-shaped shells, and short, thick back legs and feet. Their front legs are flat with scales and their heads are almost rectangular-shaped. They also have a beak.

Tortoise words: Tortoise species include the PANCAKE, INDIAN STAR, IMPRESSED, ASIAN FOREST, SPECKLED CAPE, SPINY SOFTSHELL, GEOMETRIC and GALAPAGOS TORTOISE (the largest of all the species). A baby tortoise is called a HATCHLING.

Did you know? 1: The scales on a tortoise's legs are called scutes.

Did you know? 2: Both their head and legs can be withdrawn into their shell for protection.

Did you know? 3: Tortoises are well-known for living very long lives – sometimes even 200 years plus.

Collective noun possibilities: CREEP

129. TURTLE

Description: Famous for their long lifespans, turtles are aquatic reptiles and are related to tortoises and terrapins. They have a hard shell, hard beak, webbed feet and a tail. Some species have eyes and nostrils on the top of their head, which help them to hide better in water.

Turtle words: There are two major groups of modern turtles – SIDE-NECKED TURTLES and HIDDEN NECK TURTLES – named according to the way their head retracts. Species include RED-EARED SLIDERS, YELLOW-BELLIED SLIDERS, EASTERN BOX TURTLES, WESTERN PAINTED TURTLES, MISSISSIPPI MAP TURTLES and COMMON MUSK TURTLES (aka STINKPOTS).

Did you know? 1: Depending on the species, a turtle's shell can either be streamlined, flat or crested.

Did you know? 2: A turtle cannot come out of its shell as its shell is connected to its body.

Did you know? 3: In some species of turtle, lower temperatures in the environment lead to male turtles hatching and higher temperatures to females hatching.

Collective noun possibilities: BALE

130. TYRANNOSAURUS REX

Description: Tyrannosaurus Rex (also known as T-Rex) was a large theropod dinosaur – and is by far the most popular type of dinosaur to be portrayed in films, books etc. It had a long muscular tail, short, clawed arms and a huge head. At about 6 metres tall and 12 metres long, the T-Rex really was frightening!

T-Rex words: There may have actually been three species of tyrannosaurus – REX, IMPERATOR, and REGINA. The differences between the species are to do with their teeth and femur variations. Tyrannosaurus Rex means TYRANT LIZARD KING.

Did you know? 1: The T-Rex was one of the smartest dinosaurs, its brain being at least twice as big as other large carnivorous dinosaurs.

Did you know? 2: The T-Rex had 50 – 60 huge teeth and an incredibly powerful bite. The largest T-Rex tooth ever found was 30cm long.

Did you know? 3: The most complete T-Rex skeleton found so far was discovered in South Dakota and was nicknamed Sue. Sue was sold for £5,000,000 in 1997 to a museum in Chicago.

Collective noun possibilities: TERROR

131. UNICORN

Description: Unicorns are legendary creatures that are found in many stories around the world. They resemble elegant horses, but with an additional single, spiralling horn projecting from their head. Traditionally, a unicorn is shown as being white, but its image varies and has also changed over time.

Unicorn words: The QILIN is the Chinese version of a unicorn. Rather than having the body of a horse, it has the body of a tiger or deer, but always with a single horn. A baby unicorn is a FOAL or a SPARKLE.

Did you know? 1: Unicorns have a variety of mystical powers. Some have manes that can make them invisible, others can fly, and the power of their blood is sometimes mentioned too. They can also often purify water with the touch of their horn. Seeing a unicorn is believed to bring good fortune.

Did you know? 2: They are said to live deep within enchanted forests.

Did you know? 3: Unicorns symbolise innocence, beauty, grace, rarity, strength, freedom and courage. The unicorn became a significant symbol of purity and power in Scotland in the 15th century and is Scotland's national animal.

Collective noun possibilities: BLESSING

132. VELOCIRAPTOR

Description: Velociraptors were sickle-clawed, bipedal (two-footed) dinosaurs that were alive towards the end of the Cretaceous Period. They were thought to be feathered, however their arms would have been too short for flying. They also had long, muscular shins, and a long claw on the second toe of each foot. They had 26-28 serrated teeth and grew to be about the size of a wolf.

Velociraptor words: Velociraptor comes from the Latin words 'VELOX', meaning 'SWIFT', and 'RAPTOR', meaning 'ROBBER' - and they were likely to have been very effective hunters.

Did you know? 1: Velociraptors had a number of bird-like qualities, including swivel-jointed wrists, hinged ankles, forward-facing toes, wishbones, and also hollow bones (making them light-weight and fast).

Did you know? 2: Scientists think that they hunted solo, possibly at night.

Did you know? 3: Although they were probably one of the more intelligent dinosaurs (their brain being quite large relative to their body), they probably weren't as intelligent as they are sometimes made out to be.

Collective noun possibilities: PACK

133. VULTURE

Description: A vulture is a bird of prey that scavenges on carrion. It has wide, strong wings, relatively weak legs, blunt talons, a powerful beak, and an almost feather-free neck and head (which helps to prevent that area from becoming matted with blood when feeding).

Vulture words: There are OLD WORLD VULTURES (those found in Africa, Asia and Europe) and NEW WORLD VULTURES (those found in North, Central and South America). The BLACK VULTURE is the largest vulture and is also generally considered to be the largest bird of prey (about 1 metre tall).

Did you know? 1: Vultures have a digestive system containing special acids that are strong enough to fight against anthrax, botulism and cholera bacteria.

Did you know? 2: They sometimes hunch their bodies and tuck in their heads when it's cold. In the heat, they will sometimes stretch their necks and open their wings out wide.

Did you know? 3: In some cultures, vultures have long had a bad reputation – perhaps for various reasons: they're not the most attractive of birds, they have uncouth habits, and they scavenge on carrion that other animals have worked hard to kill. In some ancient cultures, however, vultures have a more positive reputation. Either way, they do help to keep the environment clean!

Collective noun possibilities: WAKE, KETTLE, COMMITTEE

134. WALRUS

Description: A walrus is a large, flippered marine mammal with whiskers and tusks (both males and females). Walruses can grow up to 12 feet long and their tusks to around 3 feet. They also have useful pharyngeal pouches (air sacs on their throats) that they can inflate like pillows, allowing them to bob up and down while keeping their heads above water.

Walrus words: Walruses are PINNIPEDS, meaning 'FINS FOR FEET' and are sometimes called the GIANTS/KINGS OF THE ARCTIC. There are two subspecies: ATLANTIC and PACIFIC WALRUSES.

Did you know? 1: Walrus' tusks have a variety of uses: to fight other walruses and predators, to help them climb out of the water, and to keep breathing holes open in the ice.

Did you know? 2: Walruses need lots of blubber to keep warm as they often have to cope with very low temperatures.

Did you know? 3: Their only natural predators are orcas and polar bears.

Collective noun possibilities: HERD, HUDDLE

135. WASP

Description: Wasps are stinging insects, usually with slender, smooth legs and body, a very narrow waist, and a pointed lower abdomen. They have 5 eyes (2 compound and 3 simple) and come in many different colours, including bright red, green, metallic blue, and orange – as well as the classic yellow and black. They have biting mouthparts and only the females have stingers.

Wasp words: Wasp species include the RED, NORWEGIAN, TREE, PAPER, GALL and SAXON WASP. One type of wasp that is especially aggressive and gives a particularly painful sting is the GERMAN YELLOW JACKET. There are two wasp subgroups: SOCIAL and SOLITARY.

Did you know? 1: Unlike bees, wasps are predatory creatures – and as a result, natural pest controllers. They help get rid of lots of different insects and spiders etc. and are great for the ecosystem.

Did you know? 2: Many wasp species create their own paper to build their nests by chewing up wood then spitting it out as pulp to be shaped accordingly.

Did you know? 3: Wasp venom contains pheromones that can easily make other nearby wasps more aggressive. Swatting a wasp near to its nest or close to other wasps is best avoided for this reason. Unlike bees, wasps don't die after they sting.

Collective noun possibilities: SWARM, NEST, COLONY

136. WEREWOLF

Description: Werewolves are often shown as having no tail, being larger than a real wolf and having a human voice and eyes.

Werewolf stories: Werewolf legends go back as far back as The Epic of Gilgamesh, and the Greek myths. In one Greek myth, KING LYCAON is turned into a werewolf by the god, Jupiter. European belief in LYCANTHROPY (the state of being a werewolf) developed at around the same time as a belief in witches. Some murderers around this time (e.g. MICHAEL VERDUN and GILES GARNIER), committed such awful crimes that either they or others claimed that they had only acted in such ways when they were in a werewolf state.

Did you know? 1: In folklore, a werewolf is a human who shape-shifts into a wolf-like creature, either on purpose or under a curse or enchantment. Being bitten by a werewolf or drinking rain water from a werewolf's paw-print are apparently both effective ways of becoming one yourself.

Did you know? 2: Werewolves are usually said to transform into bloodthirsty beasts on the night of a full moon, at which point they become unable to control their desire to kill.

Did you know? 3: Despite most people now believing that werewolves are mythical creatures, sightings are still reported each year...

Collective noun possibilities: LUNACY

137. WHALE

Description: Whales are fully aquatic marine mammals with large, streamlined bodies. Most tend to be various shades of grey and are sometimes also a combination of blue, black and white. Size varies greatly, and some species are huge. All whales have one or two blowholes on top of their head.

Whale words: Whale species include the BLUE, HUMPBACK, MINKE, BELUGA, FIN, SPERM, and KILLER WHALE. Whales fall into two main categories: BALEEN WHALES (with a baleen plate to sieve krill, plankton and crustaceans) and TOOTHED WHALES (enabling them to eat larger prey).

Did you know? 1: Whales are well-known for the sounds they make and especially for one of their methods of communication: echolocation. Because of their whistles, clicks and chirps, beluga whales are sometimes nicknamed the 'canaries of the sea'. Male humpback whales sing complex songs that can last up to 20 minutes and can be heard several miles away.

Did you know? 2: The blue whale is the largest animal that has ever lived – weighing as much as 24 elephants and measuring up to 90 feet long.

Did you know? 3: Whales are conscious breathers, meaning that they actively choose when to take a breath. Their breathing involves their blowhole/s and their lungs.

Collective noun possibilities: POD – although only some whales are social

138. WOODPECKER

Description: Woodpeckers are striking, colourful birds that are well-known for pecking tree trunks with their pointy beaks. They also have zygodactyl feet – two toes facing forwards and two facing backwards on each foot – which helps them more easily climb and grasp vertical trees.

Woodpecker words: Woodpecker species include the GREATER SPOTTED, LESSER SPOTTED, RED-BELLIED, IVORY-BILLED, SAPSUCKER and BROWN FRONTED WOODPECKER. A famous cartoon woodpecker is WOODY WOODPECKER.

Did you know? 1: Woodpeckers wrap their long tongue around the back of their head when they are engaged in high-speed tree pecking. This helps to protect their brain as well as giving them somewhere to store their tongue. They create a new nest hole each year.

Did you know? 2: They don't wear out their beaks despite all the pecking they do (up to 20 pecks per second and 8,000 – 12,000 pecks a day). This is due to the chisel-like shape of their beaks and the fact that their beaks are always growing.

Did you know? 3: The drilling or drumming noises that woodpeckers make are also sometimes for communication – to attract a mate or to announce their territory.

Collective noun possibilities: DESCENT, HAMMER, STRIKE, KNOCK

139. WORM

Description: Worms are cold-blooded, limbless invertebrates, mainly with a long tube-like, flattened or leaf-like body. They have light receptor cells but no actual eyes. They also don't have lungs, but instead breathe through their skin. Some worms have a thickened section towards their head, which contains a special type of mucus that they secrete in order to form a cocoon for their embryos.

Worm words: Worms include TAPEWORMS, ROUNDWORMS, FLATWORMS, PINWORMS, HOOKWORMS, THREAD WORMS, RIBBON WORMS, BOOTLACE WORMS and EARTHWORMS.

Did you know? 1: Worms can become paralysed if exposed to the light for too long.

Did you know? 2: They can regrow some parts of their body if needed.

Did you know? 3: Charles Darwin suggested that worms might be the most important creatures on earth as they aerate the soil and help to make it fertile.

Collective noun possibilities: BED, BUNCH, CLAT, WRIGGLE, SQUIRM

140. ZEBRA

Description: Zebras look a lot like black and white stripy horses and are part of the same genus. They have a long neck and head and a short mane.

Zebra words: The three living species of zebras are the IMPERIAL, PLAINS and MOUNTAIN ZEBRA. In Roman circuses, the zebra was often called a TIGER-HORSE or HORSE-TIGER. Crossed with other members of the horse family, they become ZEBRIODS.

Did you know? 1: The function of zebra stripes has long been debated and researched, and there are still several theories: 1. Protection from flies that bite – as some flies have been shown to land less often on stripy surfaces; 2. Thermoregulation – as black absorbs heat and white reflects it; 3. To hide from/confuse predators, and 4. To better recognise each other – as each pattern of stripes is unique.

Did you know? 2: Zebras sometimes run in a zigzag pattern when chased, making it harder for predators to catch them.

Did you know? 3: Zebras communicate with loud brays, barks and gentle snorts.

Collective noun possibilities: DAZZLE, HERD, ZEAL

SCORESHEETS

The number of rounds you play for each game is entirely up to you. The scoresheets on the following pages provide some options. You can either copy one of these suggestions, print out a scoresheet from our website, or make up your own version. Each round usually takes about five to ten minutes.

POINTS REMINDER

» 1 point for every vote received

» -1 point per person for any canary clones – when 2 or more people invent the same name

» 2 points extra if you're the cat that got the canary – when everyone votes for you

EXAMPLE SCORESHEET

	Name Sophia	Name Ellen	Name Arthur	Name Oscar	Name Harvey	Name May
Round 1 Pig + Parrot	1	0	2	0	3	0
Round 2 Badger + Tortoise	0	0	0	6 + 2	-1	-1
Round 3 Cow + Owl	2	2	0	1	1	0
Round 4 Elephant + Fairy	1	2	2	0	0	1
FINAL SCORES	4	4	4	9	3	0

MINI POP!T

	Name	Name	Name	Name	Name	Name
Round 1						
Round 2						
Round 3						
Round 4						
FINAL SCORES						

STANDARD POP!T

Name	Name	Name	Name	Name	Name

Round 1

Round 2

Round 3

Round 4

Round 5

Round 6

Round 7

FINAL SCORES

LONG POP!T

	Name	Name	Name	Name	Name	Name
Round 1						
Round 2						
Round 3						
Round 4						
Round 5						
Round 6						
Round 7						
Round 8						
Round 9						
Round 10						
FINAL SCORES						

WE HOPE YOU ENJOY PLAYING CANARY POP!T WITH FRIENDS AND FAMILY
YOU CAN HELP US AND THE ANIMAL ORGANISATIONS WE SUPPORT
BY LEAVING A REVIEW AND BY TELLING OTHERS ABOUT CANARY POP!T

VISIT BAGGYWRINKL.COM TO FIND OUT MORE
AND TO DISCOVER OUR OTHER CREATIVE GAMES AND KITS

https://baggywrinkl.com/

Made in the USA
Middletown, DE
08 September 2022